MICRO ADVENTURE™

#5
MIND-
BENDERS

by
Ruth Glick
and
Eileen Buckholtz

A Parachute Press Book

SCHOLASTIC INC.
New York Toronto London Auckland Sydney Tokyo

Book was designed by Gene Siegel.
Program 7 was designed by David Baggett.

ISBN 0-590-33169-8

12 11 10 9 8 7 6 5 4 3 2 1   10 4 5 6 7 8 9/8

Printed in the U.S.A.   01

Warning: The following information is crucial to the success of your mission. Read it carefully. It may save your life.

As a certified member of ACT (the Adventure Connection Team) your job, as always, is to defend the cause of good against evil. It won't be easy, because BRUTE (the Bureau of Random Unlawful Terror and Evil), an international organization bent on wreaking havoc throughout the world, will be fighting you every step of the way. Your computer expertise will be vital to this mission. So turn on your home system. Throughout this adventure you'll be called upon to program it to get the ACT team out of some really tough spots.

Look for the chart next to the program instructions. It will tell you which micros will run each program. If the program won't run as is on your computer, consult the Reference Manual in the back of the book — fast! Good luck. This message will be erased from memory in 30 seconds.

CHAPTER

1

ACT is really a top-notch organization, you think, settling back in your luxuriously padded seat. Not only do they send you on incredible adventures, but, if you come back alive, they really show their appreciation.

So here you are in the first-class cabin of a 747 heading for a week of fun in the sun. After your narrow escape on that last time-travel mission, when you didn't know whether you'd be stuck back in the Revolutionary War or blown to smithereens by BRUTE's atomic bomb, ACT figures they owe their computer expert a little R and R.

Looking around, you notice you're in good company. Just across the aisle is Senator Macklin. For him, this trip must be business, not pleasure. Something about a high-level energy conference he's setting up with some oil sheiks, you remember.

You're deciding between the duck-under-glass and the beef Wellington when two tough-looking men burst out of the front of the cabin. One is holding a wicked-looking machine gun, the other a grenade. Somehow you know they didn't order their equipment from the Astro Toy Catalog.

"We're taking over this plane," the taller one growls, pulling the pin on the grenade and pressing his thumb over the firing mechanism. "If I let up on this thing, it's curtains for everybody."

The other gestures toward the flight attendant. "Tell the captain we want to land in Grand Paloma."

Just your luck. A hijacking. The hair on the back of your neck rises as you watch the grenade's firing mechanism twitch. In less than five minutes the hijackers have the whole plane secured. You may be the only one on board who's capable of doing something. After all, you're a member of ACT — an organization that handles crises on a daily basis.

Taking a deep breath, you try to calm the pounding of your heart so you can hear yourself think. There must be some plan you can put into action. But what? You come up with a dozen scenarios and reject them all.

Suddenly a low beep and a flashing light catch your attention. They're coming from the

ACT computer you stowed in the seat pouch in front of you. Stealthily, you turn off the alarm, slide the unit onto your lap, and take a peek at the display, hoping that the guy with the grenade doesn't glance your way.

TPDBKR
LPFLK AL KLREFKD RL QRLM
REFQ EFGSNHFKD

With fingers stiff from fear, you key in a program that will decode the garbled message you've just received.

Type the following program into your computer and run it. Lines 10, 20, 90, and 140 should each be typed as one line. Now enter the secret message one line at a time.

PROGRAM 1

```
10 B$="ABCDEFGHIJKLMNOPQRSTUV
      WXYZ ."
20 A$="SUNABCDEFGHIJKLMOPQRT
      VWXYZ ."
30 N$=""
40 PRINT "ENTER LINE OF MESSAGE"
50 INPUT M$
60 L=LEN(M$)
70 FOR I=1 TO L
80 FOR K=1 TO 28
```

```
90 IF MID$(M$,I,1)=MID$(A$,K,1)
      THEN 110
100 NEXT K
110 N$=N$+MID$(B$,K,1)
120 NEXT I
130 PRINT N$
140 PRINT "MORE MESSAGES TO
      DECODE, Y OR N"
150 INPUT R$
160 IF R$="Y" THEN 30
170 END
```

IBM	Apple		Radio Shack		Commodore		TI	Atari
PC & PCjr	II+	IIe	TRS-80	Color	64	VIC-20	99/4A	400/800
✓	✓	✓	✓	✓	✓	✓		

This program will run on all the personal computers checked in the chart above. See the Reference Manual, page 96, for changes for TI and Atari.

Did you do it right? you wonder. Or is this some kind of BRUTE trick? You can't imagine why ACT would instruct you *not to interfere with this hijacking.* How could they even know about it?

But before you can figure that one out, the guy with the machine gun sees you trying to slip the computer back into the pouch.

He marches down the aisle and yanks you out of your seat. "No more tricks, kid," he growls. "You're coming with us." Then his eyes fall on Senator Macklin. "And you, too, buddy. We need another insurance policy."

The hijacker's grimy fingernails are digging painfully into your shoulder. As he leans down to leer at you, you draw back. His fierce expression, accented by a two-day growth of beard, gives you the creeps. But there's something about his eyes that looks familiar. Could he possibly be a BRUTE agent you've encountered on one of your missions?

You're still trying to figure it out as the plane makes an abrupt landing at the Grand Paloma airport.

Holding you and Senator Macklin as shields, the hijackers start across the runway. Suddenly a loudspeaker booms, "Hostages, run for your lives. We've got them covered."

CHAPTER
2

Your captors seem momentarily dazed by this hitch in their plans. While they go for their guns, you and Senator Macklin wrench away. Luckily, the hijackers start shooting at the troops who have surrounded them — and not at you.

Sprinting for cover, you hear the fire of machine guns. From the safety of an airplane hangar, you turn to see the two hijackers lying lifeless on the ground. Gently, a government official leads you away.

You've barely had time to catch your breath when a dapper little man in a white suit and a Panama hat bustles into the lounge where you and Senator Macklin are recovering from your ordeal.

Following directly on his heels is one of

the hijackers you just saw looking rather dead on the runway.

"Well done, Orion," the official says, using your ACT code name. He puts his hand on the hijacker's shoulder and continues, "I'm sure you remember the Chameleon."

You shake your head with a smile. "Remembering him isn't the problem. Recognizing him is."

The last time you worked with the Chameleon he helped you free a computer buddy of yours from BRUTE's clutches. Even though the two of you worked closely, it's impossible to identify him now. The Chameleon's own personality is as bland as cottage cheese, but when he takes on a role, he literally becomes the character he's playing. His own mother would have sworn that the guy with the grimy clothes and the machine gun was a hijacker, and certainly not her son.

The senator's angry voice interrupts your thoughts. "What's going on here?"

"A little ruse to save your life, Senator," the man in the white suit replies. "Let me introduce myself. I'm Conrad Clawson, the Caribbean ACT coordinator."

"I don't know why ACT would be interfering in my business," Macklin shoots back, "but if you're really part of that organization, let's see some proof."

The senator may need proof, but you don't. You've been involved in so many weird assignments since you joined the Adventure Connection Team that nothing surprises you, least of all the appearance of the Chameleon.

Now you look up to see him grinning. "It may take Clawson all morning to straighten out the senator. Let me buy you a soda, and I'll give you the executive overview."

Seated at a table in the corner, the Chameleon begins: "Clawson didn't know you were on that plane until after he saw the passenger list. You're such a good agent that we were afraid you were going to mess up our plans. That's why we sent that message. But having you on that plane was a lucky break for ACT. We'll really need a computer expert on this mission."

Well, so much for your vacation, you think. When duty calls, you've got to answer. Besides, you're a sucker for adventure.

"I suppose you know about the energy conference the senator is coordinating on Corona," the Chameleon continues. "Well, some scary things have been going on down there over the past few weeks. A lot of VIPs have come back from vacations there acting pretty strange."

"What do you mean?" you ask. Across the room you can hear Clawson and Macklin having a heated discussion.

"Every one of them has been making erratic and uncharacteristic policy decisions. The president of a hamburger chain gave away the recipe for their secret sauce. A dyed-in-the-wool environmentalist signed over the rights to strip-mine half the Rocky Mountains. And a coach in the National Football League tried to get Yogi Berra for his first-round draft choice.''

Your eyes widen. ''All of those people visited Corona in the past few weeks?''

''Affirmative. And now Macklin's running an energy conference there, with a guest list that includes representatives from every major oil source in the world — Texas oil barons, the Russians, whoever's drilling in the North Sea, and *all* of the Arab oil sheiks. Even Nissil El Blat's coming, and he hasn't left his palace in 15 years. If this group returns making strange decisions, we could be in for World War III.''

You're about to ask a question when the ''discussion'' on the other side of the room becomes so loud that you can't ignore it anymore. You watch as Clawson pulls out an ACT briefing folder and shoves it in Macklin's face. As the senator reads he shuts up for the first time in 15 minutes. When he looks up, you notice that his skin has turned a peculiar shade of green.

''You mean, I might have come back from Corona advocating the sale of Alaska to the Communist bloc? And El Blat — what crazy things might he have tried?''

Clawson shrugs. ''Who knows? But I'm glad you finally understand the danger. We think that every VIP leaving Corona is under some sort of mental control. It's as if they've been brainwashed. But brainwashing takes a long time. This seems to happen overnight."

"But why did you have to pull this crazy hijacking stunt?" Macklin asks. "Why couldn't you come to my office?"

"Believe me, we tried. But your secretary just got back from a preconference trip to Corona. Need I say more?"

The senator looked sick before, but now he looks as if he could use intensive care. "Thanks for giving it to me straight," he mumbles. "At least I know the worst of it."

"Unfortunately that's not all," Clawson contradicts, dimming the lights and bringing up an aerial reconnaissance slide on a projector. "See this dark area in the water, right off Corona's coast? We think it's an underwater laboratory. It could be producing anything from weapons to drugs."

"How come you don't know for sure?" the senator questions.

"Because every special agent sent down there to investigate it has mysteriously disappeared."

Clawson runs through some more slides, but you're not watching anymore. There's a tight feeling in your chest as you think about all those ACT agents who vanished.

"This is too important to give up on," Clawson is saying. "We've just sent down another covert operative, and we're going to back him up with a crack team. We want you to join them."

"Now let me get this straight," the senator begins. "You hijacked me on the way to Corona in order to give me the chance to go down there with an ACT team and risk my life? I must be crazy, but I'm going to accept."

"Good man!" the Chameleon exclaims. You look at him and gasp. The two-day stubble and grubby clothes are gone. Instead, he's dressed in crisp white pants and a navy blazer with a silk ascot at the neck. On his head is a jaunty naval officer's cap. He's transformed himself into . . .

"Scarf Windhammer," he supplies. "America's Cup winner and yachtsman par excellence. But if I'm going to be sailing my 60-foot schooner into Corona harbor tomorrow afternoon, I'd better be leaving. Bye."

Clawson grins. "Just a second, Scarf. Haven't you forgotten something?"

The mariner looks up with the haughty expression he reserves only for landlubbers. "Yesss?"

You hear the door behind you close, and turn to see a young blonde woman who's either a model or a beauty-contest winner. "Scarf, darling, how lovely of you to invite me along for a little sail," she says.

Scarf doesn't even miss a beat. "My pleasure," he drawls and then turns back to the group. "I'd like you all to meet Crystal, a distinguished chemist and scuba-diving instructor who is one of ACT's most valuable assets."

The senator looks as if he's ready to sign up for scuba-diving lessons on the spot. However, Scarf has other plans. "Crystie," he exclaims, linking his arm with hers, "we're going to be late if we don't set sail with the tide." He turns to you and the senator. "See you soon." And with that they're both gone.

"You two have to be leaving also," Clawson says. "We want you to gather as much information as possible before Scarf and Crystal arrive. Your rendezvous point will be at the guests' social hour tomorrow afternoon."

"Just a second," you say. "How will we make contact with the other agent?"

"Oh, he'll be in touch," Clawson assures you. "But be on the lookout for a guy in evening clothes and a black cape."

"I didn't realize Dracula had joined ACT," you quip.

"Oh, he's better than Dracula," Clawson promises. "He's Marlow the Magnificent — and he's headlining the show at the resort's Copa Room. Lucky for us he's a magician, *and* a PhD psychologist."

A magician, you think. *What will ACT come up with next?* But from what you've heard about this mission, you may need a little magic to unravel the mystery of what's going on in Corona — and live to tell about it.

CHAPTER
3

Too bad you're at the Corona International Resort on assignment and not for a vacation, you lament the next morning. You're enjoying your third trip to the breakfast buffet — fresh pineapple, strawberry waffles à la mode, and chocolate chip muffins.

At the end of the feast, instead of paying with money, you simply insert a guest credit card in one of the computers at the door. It displays not only the charge for your meal, but also the status of your account. You've never been in such an automated hotel. Last night you registered by logging in on a terminal. It provided the card that opens your room door and gives you access to activities and services all over the resort complex — everything from four huge swimming pools and parasailing to speedboats and miniature golf. But duty calls. You're supposed to be checking this place out, you remind yourself.

After slipping into shorts and a shirt that says *I Love Corona,* you wander around, trying to look as carefree as everybody else.

The hotel's grounds are incredible. As you stroll down a shady path, past banana and coconut trees, you can smell the salt breeze blowing in from the ocean. If this isn't paradise, you don't know what is. No wonder it's one of the most exclusive vacation spots in the world.

And then you remember what Clawson told you about the scores of VIPs who've come back from this place somehow changed. The thought gives you the creeps. Corona is beautiful, all right, but it's a deadly beauty.

Casually, you continue to explore, not knowing exactly what you're looking for. Then, off in a far corner of the wide lawn, you spot a pavilion shaped like a pagoda. Its walls are paneled in red-and-gold lacquer, and a dragon-shaped banner flies from its roof. It reminds you of an elaborate Chinese tea house. Curious, you walk up to it. The sign on the door says VIDEO GAME ARCADE. But there's a CLOSED FOR REPAIRS notice tacked up over that.

You're just about to turn away when you hear unmistakable electronic noises inside. There must be a whole bunch of people in there playing video games. Maybe the place really is open, and someone just forgot to remove the sign. But when you try the door, it's locked.

Suddenly that sixth sense you've learned to trust starts to tingle. Something strange is going on here, and you're going to find out what it is.

Quickly, you duck into the low hedge at the side of the pavilion and circle the building. There are no other doors — and no windows either. You've almost given up hope of getting in when you spot a seam in the wall that joins two gold panels. At the edge of the seam is a tiny metal knob.

You pull, and one of the panels swings open. Inside, you find yourself behind a black curtain.

"What was that, Big Al? Did you see a light flash?" a gruff voice questions nearby.

"It's just the games, you dummy," replies someone who sounds even nastier.

Lifting the curtain, you sneak a look. At first all you can make out are flashing colors at the video display terminals. However, when your eyes become accustomed to the darkness, you see the room is indeed full of players lined up in front of the terminals. And they're not alone. Standing between the machines are muscular guards, dressed in khaki shorts and packing mean-looking pistols. You're trying to make sense of the scene when the guard you've identified as Big Al points his gun at a player across the room.

"That one's flunked the test," he growls. "Put him over with the rejects."

Immediately, two bruisers yank the player away from his machine and march him over to the side of the room where three women are already standing. The man doesn't try to struggle or even argue. Even more bizarre, except for the guards, everyone in the arcade is silent.

You've got to find out what's going on. And since you're not six feet tall and dressed in khaki, the only way to do it is pretend you're one of the players.

You've just stepped from behind the curtain when one of the guards notices you. "Hey, what's this one doing over here? Do you think there's a problem with the control mechanism?" he questions.

"Only one way to find out," Big Al says. Grabbing your shoulder, he shoves you into one of the lines. "Remember," he warns, "if they can't get the answers right, the treatment didn't take."

"Yeah." His buddy chuckles wickedly. "And then they're no good for anything except shark food."

Control mechanism? Shark food? you think, trying not to tremble. You still don't understand what's going on here. All you know is that in the last minute and a half you've moved one person closer to the front of the line. And the game they're playing doesn't resemble anything you've ever seen at a video arcade.

Cautiously, you lean forward to get a better look at the action. It's obviously a word game of some kind, where the player has to make quick responses in order to score points.

When the word *good* flashes across the screen, the guy in front of you responds with *evil*. That answer gets him one point. You watch as he types in other words — always antonyms for the ones on the screen.

But the responses aren't always the first thing *you'd* think of. The next pair really throws you for a loop. *Heaven,* the display flashes. *That's easy,* you think. But when the player scores points with *Hale,* you start to panic. Are they giving it to him even if he can't spell? Or is that a trick question only players under the control mechanism can answer?

Suddenly a guard yanks him away from the screen and pushes you forward.

"Have fun," he sneers.

You wait tensely for the first word to flash on the screen. But before it does, someone shouts from across the room, "Hey, Burt, come on over here. We're having trouble opening the shark tank."

Luckily, Burt is the guard who was standing over your machine. Maybe, just maybe, you have a chance to win at this game — if you can sneak a look at the program that's controlling it. And with the keyboard right here in front of you, you should be able to do it.

Stealthily, you break from game mode and enter BASIC. With a few keystrokes, you've got a listing of the program.

Type in the program below and note which antonyms it's looking for. Lines 30, 40, 100, 250, 270, and 290 should each be typed as one line.

PROGRAM 2

```
10 R=0
20 M=0
30 DATA GOOD,EVIL,LIFE,DEATH,
      ANGEL,DAMIAN
40 DATA SOFT,HARD,ACT,BRUTE,
      POLICEMAN,CRIMINAL
50 DATA PASS,FLUNK,HEAVEN,HALE
60 DATA ORDER,CHAOS,TRUTH,LIES
70 FOR K=1 TO 10
80 READ Q$,A$
90 CLS
100 PRINT "WHAT DOES",Q$,"MAKE
      YOU THINK OF?"
110 INPUT W$
120 IF W$=A$ THEN 180
130 PRINT "WRONG"
140 FOR L=1 TO 500
150 PRINT CHR$(6);
```

```
160 NEXT L
170 GOTO 230
180 PRINT "VERY GOOD"
190 FOR L=1 TO 500
200 PRINT CHR$(3);
210 NEXT L
220 R=R+1
230 NEXT K
240 CLS
250 PRINT "YOUR SCORE IS";R;"OUT
    OF 10"
260 IF R<K THEN 290
270 PRINT "THIS ONE IS UNDER
    CONTROL"
280 END
290 PRINT "ANOTHER ONE BITES THE
    DUST"
300 END
```

IBM	Apple		Radio Shack		Commodore		TI	Atari
PC & PCjr	ll+	lle	TRS-80	Color	64	VIC-20	99/4A	400/800
✓								

This program will run as is on the IBM. See the Reference Manual, page 97, for changes for all other computers.

The list gives you a familiar chill. So BRUTE *is* behind all this. And if you're going

20

to get out of here alive, you've got to play their game and win.

Just then, you see Burt ambling back across the room, scratching his ear with the barrel of his gun. If he catches you with the wrong display on the screen, you might end up looking down the wrong end of that barrel.

Run the BASIC program to get the game back on the screen. You'll have to play it correctly to prove to Burt and the other guards that you're under control. Type your answers in all capital letters.

CHAPTER

4

Luckily for your immediate life expectancy, you got 10 out of 10. Quickly you're led away to stand with the others who've passed.

"Big Al says don't move a muscle," the guard hisses at you.

You don't even nod. You just play statue like everybody else. Being sandwiched in among all these mannequins is eerie. They're so quiet that if they weren't breathing, you wouldn't know they were alive.

What's going to happen to the ones who failed? you wonder. The guards must have been joking. They wouldn't *really* feed people to sharks, would they?

The question is answered almost immediately when a grinding noise draws your attention to a section of floor in the middle of the room. Slowly, it slides open to reveal a huge aquarium. As you watch, a shark fin breaks the surface — and then another and another. By the way they're congregating near the edge of the floor, you get the idea the sharks know it's feeding time.

"Prime them with an appetizer, Burt," one of the guards calls out.

Grinning, Burt tosses what looks like a hindquarter of beef into the tank.

You've never seen fish move so fast. In a second the meat is reduced to a bloody stain in the water, and you have an excellent but sick idea of what's going to happen to those who've failed the test.

"All right, move the puppets out of here," Big Al orders, "and program the automatic feeder."

The guards have left your group unattended for a minute. Every cell in your body is urging you to follow the winners and escape while you can, but what about those other people? How can you leave them to the sharks? You can't.

Wondering if you'll live to regret your valor, you worm your way into the center of the loser's group.

"Big Al says march," a guard tells the winners. Instantly they snap to attention and begin to stomp out of the arcade.

A few moments later, you and the rejects are left alone, standing at the side of the shark tank in the floor. Except for a few twitches here and there, these people are pretty passive, too. But if their control mechanisms don't work, what's going to make them jump into that shark tank?

Before you can figure out how to get everyone out of here, the lock on the door snaps closed. Then, to your astonishment, the game machines around the room fold up and retract as if they were those crazy pull-down beds. The walls are now smooth as glass. There's something very ominous about the automatic redecorating.

The spooky feeling grows stronger when you hear the grinding noise again, and the floor beneath you begins to vibrate. Suddenly you realize that the shark tank is getting bigger. Or maybe it's the floor that's getting smaller. Either way, in less than five minutes, there won't be anywhere to stand except underwater.

This is it. You're dead. You're trying to say your prayers, when Big Al's parting orders pop into your head. He said to program the automatic feeder. Well, now you know what the automatic feeder is. And if somebody programmed it from in here, you ought to be able to unprogram it — if you can find the control panel.

You risk a quick look at the shark tank. It's now almost as big as an Olympic-size swimming pool. And some of the players who failed the test look as if they're about to take a dip.

"Get back!" you shout frantically. But they just sort of shuffle their feet. *Oh, great,* you think. And then you get an idea. "Big Al says move back," you try. This gets a slightly better response — at least they're not teetering on the edge anymore.

It's hard to balance on the vibrating floor, but you've got no choice. Resolutely, you begin to feel along the smooth plastic wall.

The shark tank has doubled in size when your fingers detect a tiny horizontal groove. You press against it, and a keyboard and screen pop up.

Luckily the control program is still on the screen. Time is running out. Can you do it?

Type in the program below and modify it to stop the receding floor before it serves you and the losers to the sharks. (Lines 180, 200, and 230 should be typed as one line.) Hint: Figure out which part of the program controls how wide the opening in the floor will be. If you need help, check the Reference Manual on page 99. Save the program, if you can. You're going to need it again.

PROGRAM 3

```
10 REM SHARK TANK CONTROLLER
20 CLS
30 FOR I=1 TO 10
40 PRINT "################"
50 NEXT I
60 PRINT  "YOU ARE HERE XX"
70 PRINT CHR$(11);
```

```
80 FOR I= 1 TO 11
90 PRINT "~~~~>~~~~>~~~~>"
100 PLAY "o2colb."
110 FOR J=1 TO 500
120 NEXT J
130 NEXT I
140 IF I >=11 THEN 160
150 GOTO 180
160 PRINT "YOU WERE DELICIOUS"
170 END
180 PRINT CHR$(30);
    "################"
190 FOR K=1 TO 11
200 PRINT CHR$(30);CHR$(30);
    "################"
210 NEXT K
220 LOCATE 1,25
230 PRINT "YOU'VE MADE IT TO
    SAFETY"
240 PRINT "THE DOOR IS UNLOCKED"
250 END
```

IBM	Apple		Radio Shack		Commodore		TI	Atari
PC & PCjr	II+	IIe	TRS-80	Color	64	VIC-20	99/4A	400/800
✓								

This program will run on the IBM PC and PCjr. See the Reference Manual, page 99, for changes for all other computers.

26

CHAPTER
5

One of the losers is teetering on the edge of the tank when the floor finally shudders to a halt. Quickly, you pull him back. So far, so good. But now what? The exit is still a dangerous swim away. And how long can 11 people balance along 18 inches of floor? You've got to reset this program to close the tank before somebody falls in.

Turning back to the screen, you look at the program again.

Change the program so it will close the floor and automatically unlock the exit. If you need help, see the Reference Manual, page 101.

You've never been so glad to get out of a game arcade. But what are you going to do with the people you've rescued? If you take them back to the hotel, they'll get rounded up again. And they're in no shape to be left on their own.

It takes a while, but you maneuver the group to a mango grove on the very edge of the resort grounds.

"Big Al says don't move!" you order, and give Clawson a quick call on the emergency channel. "Listen, this is a BRUTE operation," you explain and then go on to outline your problem.

"Maybe if we get their brains unscrambled, we can find out what BRUTE is up to," Clawson tells you. "We'll pick them up in a high-speed trawler. Have them on the beach, waiting for us."

"Right," you agree, wondering how you're going to hide 10 semi-zombies out there on the sand.

You're trying to come up with a cover when you spot a volleyball. That's it! They can be playing volleyball — if they're under enough control for you to organize a game. Quickly you line up five on each side of the net.

"Big Al says play volleyball," you order, tossing the ball into the right-hand court. To your relief, everybody goes into action — more or less.

Clawson's trawler seems to take forever, and you're afraid you're going to miss that rendezvous with the rest of the ACT team. But finally you spot the boat nosing in toward the beach. At last you can turn these poor turkeys over to somebody else.

A half hour later, you're relaxing at the guest social hour beside the pool. You'd be a lot *more* relaxed if Big Al weren't the lead drummer in the steel band. Suddenly you're wondering if every smiling entertainer, waiter, and busboy at this "fun" resort works for BRUTE.

Trying to look as if you're in the swing of things, you grab a glass of papaya juice and start to mingle. On the other side of the pool you spot Senator Macklin, who twitches one side of his face meaningfully in response. *Some agent he makes,* you think, ambling toward his umbrella table. By the time you reach him, Scarf and Crystal have already pulled up chairs.

You're bursting to tell everyone about the video arcade when a hand clamps down on your shoulder. Turning, you find yourself staring at a man whose beaming smile reminds you of a TV game-show host. But there's something reptilian about him — maybe it's his eyes — that spooks you. And when you look at him more closely, you see that though his face seems like a 30-year-old's, his hands are liver-spotted. They're the hands of an old man.

"I hope you're enjoying your stay," he says, grasping your palm. "I'm your social director, Damian Hale."

It takes a moment for the syllables to register as a name. *Damian — Hale*. Weren't those two words in the game association list? Your whole body is screaming for you to snatch your hand away. But instead you force yourself to smile and mumble something polite about the resort. Finally, Hale leaves your table. "What was that all about?" Scarf asks.

You glance meaningfully over at Big Al, who has left the band platform to emcee the limbo contest. "Later," you whisper.

At that moment, a waiter comes by with complimentary fruit juice for your table. Cautiously, you sniff the stuff. It smells like pineapple, but who knows what might be in it?

As if to prove your point, an ice cube floats to the surface of the liquid. You watch as it flips over to reveal a message etched in green letters: "Nightclub backstage PDQ."

CHAPTER

6

When you look up, everyone else at the table is staring into his or her drink.

"It must be from Marlow. He wants us to meet him backstage at the nightclub right away," Crystal whispers. "We'd better take separate routes." In a louder voice she excuses herself to go to her room.

One by one you leave the table to reassemble just inside the nightclub's stage door.

"Well, we're here, but where's Marlow?" Scarf asks.

He's answered by a clap of thunder and a flash of blinding, multicolored light. Before you have time to blink, a tall figure dressed in evening clothes appears.

"Sorry I'm late," Marlow apologizes, as though he's just made a normal, everyday entrance.

"How'd you do that?" the senator gasps.

"And what about that trick with the ice cubes?" Crystal adds.

Marlow pauses to adjust the gold cuff links that peek out from under the midnight black of his tuxedo. "Professional secrets," he demurs.

"Yes, well, that was quite effective," Scarf assures him. "There can't be any doubt that you're Marlow the Magnificent."

"Yes, and you must be the rest of the ACT team." As he shakes hands with each of you, he returns Scarf's ascot, the key to the senatorial washroom, Crystal's lipstick, and your pocket computer.

Scarf gives Marlow a sharp look. "That was quite impressive, but we don't have time for tricks. I think we'd better get down to business."

"On the contrary, that *was* business," Marlow replies. "Your lives may depend on my sleight of hand. In a tight spot, you may have to follow my directions exactly. I had to convince you that I know what I'm doing."

"Well, I'm convinced," you pipe up, stuffing your computer back in your pocket. "Let me tell you what I found this morning." Quickly you fill them in on the diabolical game arcade.

Marlow nods. "Actually, it makes sense. They'd have to have some way to know if the puppets they're producing are 100 proof or not.

If that arcade is the testing room, they've got to have a cover for it. Did you discover anything else there, Orion?''

"Just two other small things of interest," you say, trying to match his casual tone. "BRUTE organized this circus, and our genial host, Damian Hale, may well be the ringmaster.'' There is an awful silence as each member of the team takes in your news.

Crystal speaks first. "I've had my eye on Hale, too. You know, when he hasn't been hyping the limbo contests, he's been out deep-sea fishing. I've been wondering if he hasn't really been visiting that underwater lab ACT discovered.''

"With the energy conference only two days away, we've got to find out what's going on in that lab," Scarf interjects. "It's got to have something to do with the control mechanism.''

"Yes, and that means organizing a diving expedition," Crystal concludes, her eyes gleaming with anticipation. "And I'll need a volunteer to go with me.''

Nobody, including you, wants to make eye contact with her. Everyone is thinking about all the other ACT divers who vanished trying to get into that lab.

Crystal's next words make you wish you were back at the limbo contest. "Actually, Orion is the logical choice. Since everything at this place is computer-controlled, we've got to assume the setup down there is similar. And since I don't know a byte from a bit. . . ."

Byte, you think. Just the sound of it reminds you of sharks. And yet you know she's right. When the future of the world is at stake, you've got to put your personal fears aside.

"So when do we leave?" you ask, trying to sound enthusiastic.

"No time like the present," she chirps.

CHAPTER
7

"We've got only a few hours before sundown," Crystal notes as she helps you into your diving gear and gives you the three-minute course on underwater reconnaisance.

You're about to ask where the oxygen tanks are when Scarf hands you what looks like a three-inch plastic cylinder with a tea strainer at one end.

"This is a new experimental breathing device ACT has just developed," he explains. "It works exactly·like a fish's gill — I hope."

"You mean this thing's never been tested?" you ask.

"Just by Labrador retrievers in our simulation tanks. But ACT thought it would be perfect for this mission. It's easier to use than conventional gear. And if you make direct ear contact, you can talk underwater."

"But what if it doesn't work?" you persist. It's not the talking underwater you're worried about. It's the *breathing* underwater.

"You ought to know if it's filtering oxygen out of the water within the first 10 seconds." Scarf sounds reassuring — but maybe that's because he gets to stay in the boat.

You'd like to continue the discussion, but Crystal puts a hand on your shoulder. "Our sonar is picking up a BRUTE patrol headed in this direction. We've got to be underwater before they arrive."

Things happen so fast you don't have time to worry about the gill. Five minutes later you realize you're breathing just like one of the fish.

If this weren't a critical mission, you'd stop to enjoy it. The water is incredibly warm, clear, and blue. The fish look as if they swam out of a rainbow. And the gently swaying plants beckon you to explore this wonderland.

But Crystal tugs on your elbow and points toward an underwater rock formation. You know from the briefing that the lab is somewhere nearby, and that pile of boulders looks like a good prospect.

Swimming over, the two of you begin searching for an entrance. Twenty minutes later, you're still searching. Glancing at your diver's watch, you realize you're running out of time.

Crystal sways toward you and presses her gill against your ear. "I think we're going to have to use the portable sonar unit."

You nod, marveling at how clearly you can hear her.

"I really hate to do it," she adds, "because BRUTE might pick it up on their scanners. But there doesn't seem to be any other way. This sounding device is only short range, so we're going to have to evaluate each reading and then move to a new position and try again until we find the opening — or BRUTE arrives."

Trying to look as calm as she does, you nod and begin to fiddle with the dials.

Type in the following program. (Lines 90, 230, 240, 280, 310, 330, 380, 430, 480, and 530 should each be typed as one line.) Now run the program to try and find the entrance to the lab. The program works like a game. Every time you move on the grid, the computer will tell you if the mass is getting more dense or less dense. The entrance is where the mass is the least dense.

PROGRAM 4

```
10 RANDOMIZE
20   DIM G(5,5)
30   X =   INT(RND * 5) + 1
40   Y =   INT(RND * 5) + 1
50   IF (X = 3) * (Y = 3) THEN 30
60   G(X,Y) = 1
70   A = 3
80   B = 3
```

```
90  PRINT "YOU START IN THE MIDDLE
    AT 3,3"
100 H = ABS(X - A) + ABS(Y - B)
110 Z =  INT(RND (1) * 10) + 1
120 IF Z < 1 THEN 280
130 PRINT "ENTER MOVE"
140 PRINT "1 FOR UP"
150 PRINT "2 FOR DOWN"
160 PRINT "3 FOR RIGHT"
170 PRINT "4 FOR LEFT"
180 INPUT D
190 IF D < 1 OR D > 4 THEN 130
200 ON D GOSUB 350,400,450,500
210 IF G(A,B) THEN 310
220 H1 = ABS(X-A) + ABS(Y-B)
230 IF H > H1 THEN  PRINT "MASS
    IS LESS DENSE"
240 IF H < H1 THEN  PRINT "MASS
    IS DENSER"
250 H = H1
260 Z = Z - 1
270 GOTO 110
280 PRINT "DETECTOR HAS RUN
    OUT OF POWER"
290 PRINT "TOO BAD FOR ACT"
300 END
310 PRINT "YOU'VE FOUND THE
    ENTRANCE"
320 PRINT "SCORE ONE FOR ACT"
330 PRINT "ENTRANCE AT READING";
    A;",";B
340 END
350 IF A <= 1 THEN 380
360 A = A - 1
```

```
370   RETURN
380   PRINT "CAN'T GO UP, YOU'RE
      ABOVE THE ROCK--TRY AGAIN"
390   RETURN
400   IF A >= 5 THEN 430
410   A = A + 1
420   RETURN
430   PRINT "YOU'VE HIT THE BOTTOM
      --TRY AGAIN"
440   RETURN
450   IF B <= 1 THEN 480
460   B = B - 1
470   RETURN
480   PRINT "NO MORE ROCK TO THE
      RIGHT--TRY AGAIN"
490   RETURN
500   IF B >= 5 THEN 530
510   B = B + 1
520   RETURN
530   PRINT "NO MORE ROCK TO THE
      LEFT--TRY AGAIN"
540   RETURN
```

IBM	Apple		Radio Shack		Commodore		TI	Atari
PC & PCjr	II+	IIe	TRS-80	Color	64	VIC-20	99/4A	400/800
✓								

This program will run on the IBM PC and PCjr. See the Reference Manual, page 102, for changes for all other computers.

39

Crystal gives you a thumbs-up sign. Your computer has found the entrance to the lab. But just as you're about to explore it, you see a shadow gliding through the water. Quickly, Crystal grabs your arm and pulls you behind a clump of algae-covered rocks.

From your hiding place, the two of you watch as a small submarine settles near the entrance. Are they searching for you?

Crystal seems to have the same thing on her mind. "This looks like just a routine supply haul," she says.

You watch as several divers emerge and disappear through the secret entrance. In a few moments they reappear, carrying large waterproof cargo crates. You almost swallow your mechanical gill when you see the resort's logo on the boxes. *That proves the connection,* you think, as the submarine glides off toward shore. Whatever they're making down here is ending up at the resort. And you're willing to bet your microcomputer that it has something to do with the guests BRUTE is turning into puppets.

Instinctively, you glance at your computer screen. Lucky you looked. It's flashing an urgent message from Scarf. You've been so busy watching the BRUTE underwater show, you don't even know how long he's been trying to contact you. Your heart starts to pound as you read the message: BRUTE IS BACK — WITH A FLEET OF SHARKS. SHARK BEHAVIOR ODD. THEY'RE NOT FEEDING. MAY BE

UNDER CONTROL, LIKE THE HUMAN PUPPETS YOU SAW.

So that's how BRUTE eliminated the other ACT agents. But there's no time to appreciate the insight. You and Crystal have to get back to the boat — and fast.

You've already started for the surface when you look down and realize Crystal isn't with you. *What's she waiting for?* you wonder. And then you see she's leaving a tiny, ultrahigh-frequency transmitter by the lab entrance so that you can find it again quickly next time — if there is a next time.

In a moment Crystal is heading toward you. And directly behind her is a sleek, silver body with a hammerhead. Three more sharks follow it.

You and Crystal are as good as dead now — just like all those other agents. And then you get an idea. The sharks seem to be programmed to ignore fish and go after people. In fact, you're willing to bet they're programmed for specific people. That means they may be attracted to special equipment, and not just bodies. If you turn on the sonar unit and deep-six it, maybe the sharks will go after *that* instead of you and Crystal.

With trembling fingers, you turn the thing on, drop it, and pray.

CHAPTER

8

Like trained seals, the sharks dive for the sonar unit. And that buys you and Crystal the time you need to reach the surface. Scarf quickly pulls you aboard and heads the yacht for Corona.

Back at the hotel, the ACT members exchange information.

"There are a lot of guests around here who look as if they're listening to Walkmans — only they're not wearing headsets or earplugs," Marlow tells you.

Senator Macklin agrees. "Yeah. If you weren't looking for something strange, you'd probably miss it. But even I'm starting to recognize the symptoms."

Crystal nods and then launches into a report of what you've just discovered.

"So another shipment of BRUTE's Instant Brainwashing Elixir has just come over here," the senator muses. "I wonder what it is?" He turns to Marlow. "You're the psychologist. Do you think it's a food, or a drug, or something Hale slaps in your hand when he shakes?"

That last guess sends a shiver up your spine — and everybody else's, you suspect.

Marlow shrugs. "I wish I knew how they were doing it. It's as close to real magic as anything I've ever seen."

"We've got to find out, and soon," Crystal insists. "Otherwise, one of us could be next. And that would compromise the whole mission."

Scarf groans. "And don't forget that conference. If BRUTE gets control of those guys, the whole world could be at their mercy. What we need," he continues, "is a sample of whatever it is so that we can analyze it. But with those sharks patrolling the lab entrance, we don't have a chance. They're so efficient, they might as well be computer-controlled."

"Computer-controlled. Hey, that could be it!" you say.

"What do you have in mind, Orion?" Scarf asks.

"Well, I was just thinking, this whole resort is computer-controlled. You know — every time you have a meal or watch a movie or rent a motorscooter, you pay with your resort credit card. That means there's an audit trail of each guest's activities." You turn to Marlow. "If you and Senator Macklin can supply the names of the guests you think are affected, we can see what they've got in common.''

Crystal's blue eyes light up. ''That may tell us where the treatments take place.''

Marlow and the senator soon hand you a list of prime candidates.

There's George Martin, the congressman; Solverly White, the Chairman of the Board of Consolidated Motors; Barbara Jones, the TV anchorwoman; and Lute Deverin, the financier. If you can find out where these people have been, maybe you can figure out where the mind control is going on.

Input the following program. (Lines 10, 20, 30, 40, 80, 200, and 240 should each be typed as one line.) Run the program and enter each service code (a number between 1 and 10) of the resort service you want to audit. Try to find the service all four suspects have used.

PROGRAM 5

```
10 DATA ROOM SERVICE,MOVIE,GOLF,
   BAR,SPA
20 DATA  RESTUARANT,KENNEL,LAUN
   DRY,GIFT SHOP, PARA SAILING
30 DATA MARTIN,0-9,1-6,2-4,3-1,
   5-3,*
40 DATA JONES,2-5,5-4,6-6,3-4,
   8-2,*
50 DATA WHITE,5-5,4-2,*
```

```
60 DATA DEVERIN,6-3,1-2,5-4,*
70 DATA EOF,*
80 PRINT "ENTER SERVICE CODE
      1-10 FOR AUDIT"
90 INPUT N1
100 FOR I=1 TO N1
110 READ C$
120 NEXT I
130 RESTORE 30
140 PRINT "NOW CHECKING ";C$
150 X=0
160 READ N$
170 IF N$="EOF" THEN 240
180 READ R$
190 IF R$="*" THEN 220
200 IF CHR$(N1+48)=LEFT$(R$,1)
      THEN X=1
210 GOTO 180
220 IF X=1 THEN PRINT N$
230 GOTO 150
240 PRINT "TYPE Y FOR ANOTHER
      AUDIT"
250 INPUT A$
260 IF A$<>"Y" THEN END
270 RESTORE 10
280 GOTO 80
```

IBM	Apple		Radio Shack		Commodore		TI	Atari
PC & PCjr	II+	IIe	TRS-80	Color	64	VIC-20	99/4A	400/800
✓								

This program will run on the IBM PC and PCjr. See the Reference Manual, page 104, for changes for all other computers.

"Look at that," Scarf marvels. "I thought Marlow was the magician, but your computer deserves equal billing."

"Every one of these people has been to the health spa," Crystal says with a shudder. "I was going to take a sauna there this evening. Guess I'll cancel my plans."

Marlow's voice is unusually quiet. "Unfortunately, someone's got to check it out."

"Let's draw straws," the senator suggests. "That way we've all got an equal chance to luck out."

However, luck is not with the senator — or with you. You both draw the short sticks. Twenty minutes later, you and he are wearing fluffy white terrycloth togas, and inspecting the reception desk's list of spa offerings. As the senator rambles on about hot tubs and herbal massage, you realize that you haven't eaten since breakfast. You know you can't put off searching the spa until after dinner, but you're starving. Sitting right on the reception desk is a basket of complimentary candy bars. Maybe one will tide you over.

You tear off the wrapper and grin as you read: "WUNGO — *the candy of Corona.*" You take a bite and gag. This "candy" tastes like presweetened sawdust. What's it supposed to be, a health bar or something? But before you can warn Macklin, he takes a bite, too.

"If this is candy, I'm a termite," he sputters.

Dropping your Wungo bar into the trash, you head for the water fountain. The senator, always conscious of his public image, discreetly slips his into the pocket of his toga.

But before you can think any more about it, a red-headed attendant approaches. Dressed in a gold leotard, tights, and matching leg warmers, she looks like an Olympic gymnast.

"We're running a special on shampoos and hair styling today," she says. "I'm sure you and your friend will love it, Senator Macklin."

"No thanks," he declines graciously. "We'd just like to look around a little bit."

"Oh, I can't take no for an answer," the woman continues. From her high-pressure sales pitch, you guess that either she's working on commission or there's something funny about the shampoo here. In fact, maybe it soaks right through your hair to your brain.

"No thanks," you demur for the fifth time. "But we would like to buy a bottle of shampoo" — *to analyze,* you add silently.

Suddenly Miss Golden Girl's expression hardens. "I'm afraid I couldn't allow you to take a bottle out of here. It's a special formula the resort doesn't wish revealed."

You grab the senator's arm. "Oh, that's

okay. I think we'll just go have supper and come back later.''

"But I really can't allow you to do that either," the attendant purrs. As you start to back out the door, she rings a buzzer. Suddenly you see a meaty hand grasp the senator's other arm — and feel an iron grip on yours as well.

CHAPTER

9

Nobody else in the spa even glances up as two burly women march you and Macklin toward the styling area.

"Helga, give the senator the VIP treatment in one of the private rooms," the attendant orders. "And Olga, you give the runt the $9.95 special."

Oh no, you think, the two of you are going to be separated.

Before you can protest, Olga pushes you into one of those tilt-back chairs. But this one's got some special equipment. Olga presses a hidden button, and within seconds metal cuffs snap out, encircling your wrists and ankles. Before anyone has a chance to notice the cuffs, Olga whips out a sheet and drapes it over your body.

You're about to scream when Olga lifts the sheet. Pointing to the straight razor hanging from her belt, she hisses, "One peep out of you and I cut."

You sit very quietly.

"Don't worry, you'll feel more cooperative in a few minutes, honey," Olga assures you as she uncorks a bottle of shampoo.

You're trying to decide which is a saner risk — the razor or the shampoo — when out of the corner of your eye, you see a figure in black enter the spa. It's Marlow, dressed in full-performance regalia. As you watch, he pulls a dove out of his sleeve. The bird flies across the room, and music fills the air.

Everybody in the salon, including Olga, is transfixed as Marlow turns a bottle of shampoo into a bouquet of orchids.

"And now for my grand finale," he announces with a flourish. "I'll need a volunteer from the audience."

Ignoring the others in the salon, Marlow strides in your direction.

"You'll do nicely," he proclaims. Like magic, the manacles holding your arms and legs snap open. Shakily, you stand up.

"Watch closely," Marlow tells the audience.

"Stand right where I place you. Don't move an inch," he hisses in your ear.

As he mouths a bit of mumbo jumbo, he waves his cape over you. For an agonizing moment, you feel as though you can't breathe. And then you hear a crackle of thunder. With a sick sensation in the pit of your stomach, you feel yourself falling, falling, falling, falling. . . .

The next thing you know, you and Marlow are standing in the hotel laundry room, surrounded by carts of dirty linen.

"How did you manage that?" you ask, still dazed.

"Sorry, another professional secret." As Marlow speaks, he slaps a bottle of shampoo into your hand. "Quick, tell me what they've done with the senator. I've got to go back for him."

"They took him to the VIP room —"

Before you even finish, Marlow has disappeared in a puff of blue smoke. But his voice echoes back from thin air ". . . meet back in your room."

By the time you find your way from the sub-basement up to the guest wing of the hotel, everyone except Marlow is waiting anxiously in your room.

When you see Senator Macklin, you breathe a sigh of relief. "Did Marlow get you out?" you ask.

The senator shakes his head. "No, I slipped away in the confusion."

Just then, the door flies open and the magician rushes in. "I can't find the senator."

Then his eyes fix on Macklin. "Are you all right?" he asks.

"Certainly," the senator snaps. "Why shouldn't I be?"

"No reason," Marlow says. "We were just concerned about your safety." He turns to you. "Orion, give Crystal that bottle of shampoo so she can analyze it."

"How do you know it's the shampoo?" Scarf asks.

"I was nosing around in the spa's back room and found those crates you described being loaded into the submarine. They were filled with the stuff. That's when I hightailed it out front to rescue Orion and the senator."

You give him a crooked grin. "And are we glad you did!"

Turning to Macklin, you see he's busy munching on a Wungo bar.

"Hey, I thought you said those tasted like sawdust."

"Did I? I think you may have taken that statement out of context," the senator replies in his best press conference voice. "Actually, they're quite good."

Marlow gives you a worried look, then turns to Macklin and starts to talk in a very persuasive voice.

"Senator, I know you must be sleepy after this ordeal, very sleepy."

"Very sleepy," the senator repeats with a huge yawn.

"So it might be a good idea if you went back to your room for a rest."

The senator nods docilely and drops his Wungo bar on the table.

"Go back and lie down on your bed," Marlow adds, putting his arm around the senator. "As soon as your head hits the pillow, your eyes will close and you'll go to sleep."

"I will go to sleep," Macklin says as Marlow shoos him out the door.

"What was all that about?" Scarf demands.

"A layman might not pick up the symptoms, but Macklin's behaving like a classic brainwashing case. I'm afraid they got to him after all," Marlow answers. "And if they have, he's as dangerous to us as any BRUTE agent here."

CHAPTER
10

"I was afraid this mission was going too smoothly," Scarf groans.

"Smoothly?" you say. "I've almost been eaten by sharks twice and brainwashed once."

"Maybe we can turn this to our advantage," Marlow says soothingly. "I planted a bug on the senator. If someone from BRUTE approaches him, we'll hear their plans."

"What I want to know about is those Wungo bars," you say. "They really do taste awful, you know."

Scarf's brow wrinkles. "But I've seen a lot of people around here munching them. What do you think it means?"

"I don't know. But let's take a different approach," Crystal suggests, looking in your direction. "Since you risked your scalp to get us a sample of the shampoo, why don't we find out what's in it?''

As Crystal speaks, she opens up a large suitcase. Folded inside is a minilab that would make your chemistry teacher green with envy. It's got everything from a microscope to a miniature centrifuge.

Crystal starts with a very basic operation. Deftly, she begins to prepare a slide using a drop of the shampoo liquid.

Apparently the fancy chemistry setup impresses the Chameleon, too. You look up, expecting to see Scarf Windhammer and encounter instead —

''Dr. Von Lauer,'' he supplies, pulling a pair of wire-rimmed spectacles from the pocket of his white lab coat. As you stare in surprise, he gives you a precise little smile. ''Just so, my young friend. With my help, we will find out what is going on, no?''

Crystal is apparently used to this kind of assistance from the Chameleon. ''I certainly hope so,'' she tells him as she begins to focus the microscope. ''That's funny. I don't see anything unusual. This stuff looks like just a mild saline solution. . . . No, wait a minute, something's swimming in it. This is weird. Dr., er, uh, Von Lauer, come take a look.''

The Chameleon strides purposefully over and replaces her at the microscope. ''Verry, verry interesting,'' he murmurs.

Crystal shakes her head and then asks

eagerly, "What do you think it is?"

"It looks like an organic cell," the good doctor replies. "But it's dormant."

"Why don't I try putting it on an agar plate and see what happens," Crystal suggests. She turns to a drawer in her portable lab. But before she can find what she's looking for, the "doctor" has started a little experiment of his own. Picking up the senator's discarded Wungo bar, he breaks off a few crumbs and sprinkles them on the slide.

Even without the magnification you can see that a reaction of some type is taking place. The whole slide platform is bathed in an iridescent orange light. And the organism in question has swollen up like a raisin in a glass of water.

"What's happening?" you gasp.

Crystal rushes to focus on the slide again. "I can't believe it," she exclaims. "The thing's quadrupled its body size. And it's gobbling up those crumbs like a vacuum cleaner on high speed. That was brilliant of you to drop that stuff in there," she tells the "doctor." "What made you do it?"

"It was all those people eating Wungo bars. I deduced there had to be a reason, and maybe it was somehow tied to that shampoo."

"So now we know that something in the shampoo is alive and thrives on Wungo bars. But how does it chip away at people's minds?" Marlow wonders aloud.

His words give you the answer. "Did you say *chip away* at people's minds?"

He nods.

"Well, according to what I've been reading in the professional journals, the next step in computer technology is biological chips — little organisms that would function as computer memory circuits. . . ."

"And BRUTE's latest diabolical scheme involves implanting those chips in people's heads to control their behavior," Marlow finishes the thought.

"But I thought production models were years in the future," Crystal says.

"So did I," you agree. "But I'd be willing to bet that BRUTE has thrown all its resources into speeding up the process."

"That's got to be it," the Chameleon agrees. You notice that while you've been talking, he's changed back into Scarf. "And the chips are obviously nourished by something in those Wungo bars," he adds, straightening his ascot.

"It's probably a protein," Crystal muses. "But I'll have to do an analysis to be sure."

However, before she can even start, everyone is startled by a loud burst of static.

"What is that?" you whisper. Oddly enough, the sound seems to be coming from the red carnation in Marlow's lapel.

"It's a transmission from the bug I planted on the senator," he informs you, twisting several petals. "Here, let me tune it in."

"I'm glad you're feeling better," you hear someone tell the senator.

"That sounds like Damian Hale," Crystal says.

"Right," you confirm. "But then we knew he was in the middle of this."

"Quiet," Scarf snaps. "We've got to hear what they're saying."

"Senator Macklin, I've come to discuss the entertainment for the conference tomorrow," you hear Hale murmur in a friendly voice. "I have a great idea for a floor show. Let's feed you to a tank of hungry sharks."

"Oh, that sounds nice," Macklin agrees enthusiastically.

A diabolical laugh booms from the speaker. And when Hale addresses Macklin this time, there's a completely different note in his voice. "Well, Senator," he rasps, "there's no need to put you through the arcade test. It's clear you're under absolute BRUTE control."

There's a sick feeling in your stomach. And you have a suspicion that it's going to get worse.

Through the speaker, you hear a knock at the door, followed by the sound of heavy footsteps.

"Boss, is it time for the interrogation yet?" You'd know that voice anywhere — it's Big Al.

"You can help with the debriefing," Hale

assures him. "And then I want you to take the sub back to the lab. This batch of chips is perfect, and I'll need a supply for everyone who's arriving for tomorrow's conference. Once we've got the world oil supply under control, every country on earth becomes BRUTE's hostage."

Oh, no, you shudder. But that's not the worst of it. Hale is asking Macklin a bunch of routine questions. The last one is: "Are you affiliated with anyone else besides the U.S. Senate?"

The senator begins to rattle off a list of everything from his hometown Rotary Club to the Audubon Society and Friends of the Smithsonian.

You cross your fingers and toes, hoping against hope that he won't mention ACT. But all you get for your trouble is a cramp.

"I'd never forgive myself if I didn't mention my newest association," the senator chirps up proudly. "I've been made a special agent with the Adventure Connection Team. They sent me down here to try to find out what you had planned for the conference."

CHAPTER

11

The senator's words make you feel as if you've had the breath knocked out of you. And you know more bad news is coming when Hale asks, "Are you working with other ACT agents, and if so, who are they?"

Macklin immediately begins to rattle off the code names and physical descriptions of everyone listening at the other end of the microphone. "I left them all in Orion's room," he adds helpfully.

"Terrific. He's blown our cover," Scarf says, stating the obvious.

"That means we've got to get out of here now," Crystal says.

Instantly, you're sprinting across the room. "We've got to open the door before . . ." you shout.

But already it's too late. All eyes turn toward the lock, which has slammed home with an ominous "click."

"Computer-controlled just like everything else around here," you sigh. "They've got us." You turn hopefully to Marlow. "Unless you can pull that disappearing act you used to get me out of the spa, we're trapped!"

Marlow shakes his head sadly. "I hate to give away a professional secret, but that trick works only if there's a laundry chute nearby."

The conversation is cut off abruptly by the sound of heavy footsteps in the hall outside. You hear the lock click again.

"Listen," Marlow hisses. "I may have one ace up my sleeve. But you all have to stand absolutely still. Don't move a muscle."

You hold your breath as the door flies open, and Big Al and five guards charge into the room. You'd love to run and hide, but Marlow's last words somehow keep your feet in place.

"Look this way, gentlemen," Marlow commands, clapping his hands to get their attention.

"Gotya," Big Al growls, reaching for the magician. But before his hands can close on Marlow's shoulders, he stops in midgrasp and looks back at his men.

"Hey, that's funny," he says. "I thought that gang of ACT agents was supposed to be here. But I don't see anybody."

Your eyes widen. You and the rest of the team are standing five feet in front of him.

In that same commanding voice, Marlow adds, "There is nothing, I repeat nothing, in this room except tables and chairs."

"Hey, what's all this furniture doing up in a guest room?" one of the guards asks Big Al.

"I dunno." He shrugs.

"Turn your faces to the wall and count slowly to 2,000," Marlow instructs.

Obediently, Big Al and his cohorts turn around and start counting in unison, "1 . . . 2 . . . 3. . . ."

"Quick," Marlow whispers, "let's get out of here. My hypnotic suggestions will last only a few minutes."

"But they know who we are," Crystal says as the four of you rush down the fire stairs. "There's no place in this complex that's safe."

"Let's try for the mango grove," you suggest. "It's on the edge of the island."

In a few minutes you're leaning against a mango tree, rubbing the cramp in your side.

"Now we've got to destroy the supply of mindbender chips in that lab," Crystal says.

"You'll never find it at night," Marlow tells her. "I'm afraid it's going to have to wait till tomorrow." He turns to Scarf. "Smart thinking to moor the boat in that hidden cove. As soon as dawn breaks, you take Orion and

Crystal back out to the lab entrance. I'm going back for the senator now.''

"But you said that hypnotic suggestion was going to wear off soon,'' you remind him. "Those goons will nab you as soon as you set foot in the hotel.''

Marlow grins. "Making myself invisible is a lot easier than trying to make a whole room full of people disappear.''

You blink. Marlow seems to have disappeared in midsentence. But you hear his voice coming from the other side of the mango grove. "If I'm not on the beach by nine A.M., leave without me.''

"We can't do that,'' Crystal objects.

"You'll have to. This mission is more important than my life — or even the senator's.''

You'd like to argue, but there's no one to argue with. Marlow has vanished like a ghost in the darkness.

CHAPTER

12

Just before sunrise, you follow Scarf and Crystal to the cove where the schooner is waiting. In no time at all you've set sail, and Scarf has brought you back to yesterday's diving site.

"Well, at least it's too early for the BRUTE patrol," he observes.

"I hope it's too early for the sharks, too," you say nervously as you suit up for the dive.

Just before you dive, Scarf hands you a fancy three-color ballpoint pen.

"Is this in case I want to write in red, blue, or purple underwater?" you quip.

"No, it's a distress beacon. If you get in trouble, press the purple button."

"Thanks," you reply as Scarf helps you over the side. "I hope we won't need it."

Using the homing device that Crystal planted, you locate the entrance to the lab almost at once. You examine the door and grin. BRUTE must be so sure of their cover that they put only a simple computer lock on the door. With your portable unit, you open it in no time flat.

Quickly you swim into the lab's entry chamber, a huge water tank. The outer door whooshes closed, and suddenly you feel like a lobster in a trap. Nervously, you wait for the water to drain so the inner door will open. But nothing happens.

You put your gill up to Crystal's ear. "How do we get out of here?" you ask.

"How about those three buttons on the wall?" she suggests, pointing toward a row of buttons that has just started to glow iridescent green beside the inner door. Each one has a symbol in the center: @, #, $.

Swimming over, you have a look.

"For entry, press today's two-symbol code," a small plastic sign advises. At the bottom in even smaller letters it says, "We will not be responsible for fatalities resulting from failure to enter correct code."

Crystal, who has also read the message, swims back to the door through which you entered. But there are no handles or knobs. The only way out of here is through the door with the buttons.

"We could guess which ones to press," she suggests uncertainly.

You suspect that might be equivalent to stepping in front of a firing squad. You've seen systems like this before. You've got to guess the right symbols and press them in the right order!

Carefully, you inspect the wall beside the door and discover a small opening covered by a plastic bubble.

"This looks like a serial port," you observe. "If I can tap into the microprocessor that controls this door, we have a chance."

Quickly you do just that.

Type in the following program and study it to discover what sequence the computer is looking for. (Lines 60, 110, 140, and 170 should each be typed as one line.) Hint: You may have to look for ASCII values. There's a chart of them on page 125. You can also run a simulation program to find out what will happen if you press the buttons in the wrong order.

PROGRAM 6

```
10 RANDOMIZE
20 DIM K(2),D$(4)
30 READ D$(1),D$(2),D$(3),D$(4)
40 K(1)=36
50 K(2)=35
60 DATA OCTOPUS,ELECTRIC EEL,
      PIRANHA,BARRACUDA
70 FOR I=1 TO 2
80 PRINT "PRESS @,#, OR $ BUTTON"
90 INPUT B$
100 IF B$=CHR$(K(I)) THEN 140
110 PRINT "RELEASE",
      D$(INT(RND(1)+1))
```

```
120 PRINT "GOOD BYE ACT"
130 END
140 PRINT "SO FAR, SO GOOD"
    CHR$(7)
150 NEXT I
160 PRINT "LOCK IS OPEN"
170 PRINT "WELCOME TO HALE'S
    UNDERWATER HAVEN"
180 END
```

IBM	Apple		Radio Shack		Commodore		TI	Atari
PC & PCjr	ll+	lle	TRS-80	Color	64	VIC-20	99/4A	400/800
✓							✓	

This program will run as is on the IBM PC and PCjr and TI-99/4A. See the Reference Manual, page 106, for changes for all other computers.

If you weren't immersed in a tank of cold water, you'd be sweating as you finally press those buttons. But to your relief, the water begins to drain from the entrance tank. When it's all gone, the door slides silently open.

"Now that we're here," you say, "let's finish our business and get out quick!"

Stepping through the inner door, you find yourself in a hall that reminds you of a hospital corridor.

"What luck. Everybody must still be asleep," Crystal whispers. "Maybe we can even get out of here before they wake up."

"Don't count on it," a voice in back of you growls.

You whirl to find yourself facing a welcoming committee of Big Al and his friend, Burt. And to make things official, their guns are drawn and aimed right at your heart.

CHAPTER

13

"Congratulations, you're the first ACT agents to make it this far," Burt snickers. "Too bad the award will be posthumous. Hands over your heads. Now!"

The two of you are marched down the deathly quiet corridor. If only you could activate that distress-call pen you tucked in your belt. But there's no chance of reaching it now.

"Clever of you to get through the secured entry," Big Al says, prodding you with his gun. "But, of course, the whole system is locked so no one can enter before seven A.M. When you pushed the correct sequence, you set off the silent alarm."

Oh, great, you think. So much for being a computer whiz.

"Where are you taking us?" Crystal asks.

"To the director. He'd like to greet you personally."

As Al speaks, he pushes you through a set of double doors. You find yourself facing a wall of floor-to-ceiling windows that open on a spectacular seascape, complete with coral reefs, waving sea plants, and those rainbow fish. You suspect you haven't been brought here to admire the view.

A flutter of movement draws your attention to a desk and high-backed chair, facing away from you.

"Ah, Orion and Crystal," a hard voice says. "We've been expecting you." The plush leather chair swivels around, and you find yourself facing a glowering Damian Hale.

Crystal gasps. And you know why. Before, Hale's face was young; only his hands seemed ancient. Now his face is a mass of wrinkles, and his hair has thinned to a few steel-gray strands. It looks as if he's aged 40 years since you last saw him.

Hale's crooked smile makes his face look like a piece of cracked rawhide. "I don't have to put on a show for those lamebrain Corona tourists down here," he explains. "So there's no need for cosmetics."

"But you look so old," Crystal can't help saying.

"Would you say that if you knew that I'm 150 years old?" Hale asks.

"But that's impossible," Crystal insists.

"On the contrary. I'm the oldest living member of BRUTE. In the early nineteenth century they put me on longevity research, and over the years it's paid off. But enough talk of past triumphs. I'm sure you're far more interested in my present project — mind control, using biological chips. Only someone as long-lived as I could have devoted the time necessary to perfect the procedures." Hale speaks with a flourish, as though he expects to take you by surprise.

"We've already figured out how you're doing it," you inform him.

"And we know about the Wungo bars," Crystal adds.

"Oh, you think you're so smart, do you?" Hale cackles. "But you haven't experienced the thrill of being under BRUTE control."

If only you could activate that distress signal Scarf gave you. Your hands are inching toward the pen in your belt when Hale cuts off your only avenue of escape.

"Search them. Remove any personal items and ACT equipment," he orders.

Roughly, Big Al and Burt comply — removing everything from your portable computer to your waterproof watch and that all-important pen.

They dump everything on Hale's desk.

"Very interesting," he murmurs, giving your computer a thorough inspection. "And what's this?" he asks, picking up the pen. "Is this so you can write your memoirs in triplicate?'' He chuckles, idly clicking the buttons.

You ignore his gibe as he pushes the red and the blue — and finally the purple. Somehow you expected lights to flash and sirens to sound. But nothing seems to have happened. Maybe the thing is waterlogged after all. But then, what's it going to matter? Scarf is no computer expert. He'd never get through that water lock, anyway.

''Take them to the lab,'' Hale commands. ''They'll have a better appreciation of BRUTE's ingenuity if they can see our fabulous operation. Now be good,'' he instructs you and Crystal. ''And as a reward we may let you pick out the chips that will control your minds.''

This time you're really terrified. The worst thing you can imagine is being BRUTE's puppet, but you're not going to let Hale know it. So you will your feet to follow as Burt and Al escort you down the hall.

The lab is sterile and white, but it's far from empty. In one corner is a vat of orange solution; lining the walls are rows of bottles; and in the center of the tile floor are two tables that look as if they came from a doctor's examining room — except that they have straps.

Hale sees you eyeing them. ''We could put you to sleep before the procedure,'' he murmurs. ''But that spoils the fun. You don't know how much enjoyment I get out of the moment when the patient's eyes cloud.''

You bite your lip, determined not to crack. But it's all you can do to keep from screaming as the two guards push you and Crystal onto the tables and secure the straps.

"I'll just get two chips from the nutrient solution," Hale says, turning to the tank in the corner.

Hale is having the time of his life. He's relating every minor detail of the procedure. In the next five minutes you learn that BRUTE has installed the world's first underwater supercomputer to support Hale's lab, and that he has 14 billion bytes of on-line storage to hold his notes. That's more than the Social Security Administration and the IRS combined.

Hale is inspecting a chip under the microscope when the door opens, and another guard enters. With a three-inch scar down the side of his face, he looks even crueler than the others you've come up against. Scarface strides into the room and hands Hale a message.

You see his eyes flash. "Trouble above?" he questions. "What kind of trouble?"

The new guard flicks you a look as though he doesn't want to say anything in front of two ACT agents, even if they're strapped down on operating tables. "I'd prefer to discuss this in the hall, sir," he says.

Hale scowls. "All right. But this better be important."

A reprieve, you think. But what good is it? You're still strapped down.

Moments later, the new guard returns. "Hale wants to see you right away," he tells Al and Burt.

"What about the prisoners?"

"I'll take care of them," he says.

Burt and Al turn toward the door. Your eyes widen as the new guard pulls out a needle gun and silently shoots each man in the back of the neck. They go down with a thud.

Gun raised, the wild-eyed guard turns and starts advancing on the two of you.

Has he gone berserk? you wonder, straining to break free. But the straps hold you firmly in place. The guard leans over so that the scar on his cheek is only inches from your nose. And then, to your disbelief, he reaches up and peels the scar right off his skin. At the same time, his features undergo a startling transformation. Right before your eyes, all the hard lines seem to smooth out. And suddenly you're staring into the familiar face of the Chameleon.

"Got your distress call," he says with a chuckle as he begins to release your straps. "Been waiting long?"

"Long enough," Crystal answers. "Another three minutes and we would have been Hale's puppets." She gulps. "Hey, what did you do with him, anyway?"

"Same thing I did with the guards," the Chameleon replies. "Nailed him with my tranquilizer gun. He's out there in the hall, sleeping like a baby."

"Too bad it's as innocent as that," Crystal mumbles. "There are times when I wish the ACT code didn't forbid unnecessary violence. Sometimes it puts us at a disadvantage."

"But think about how much better you sleep at night," the Chameleon teases as he sets to work on her straps.

You rub your wrists as your rescuer looks around the lab. "Quite a setup," he muses. His features have already molded themselves firmly back into those of Scarf Windhammer.

"How did you ever get in here?" Crystal asks. "Even with his computer expertise, Orion had a tough time breaking the door code."

Scarf grins. "I hitched a ride with a minisub and came in with a crew of divers. But in case you're worried, they're all in dreamland, too." Quickly he glances at his watch. "But we have only 30 minutes before those sleeping uglies wake up."

Crystal is already off the table. "I can destroy the current supply of chips," she offers. "But more important than that, we need to wipe out their records so Hale can't duplicate his research." As she speaks, she's already striding across the room toward the shelves of re-agent bottles on the wall.

"How convenient," she says. "Hale's got enough chemicals here to poison everyone at the resort. They should do the trick on those microscopic chips as well. After all, they are organic."

"I think I'd better find Hale's main console," you say. "Otherwise I won't have time to wipe out all his data."

"I'll help you find the computer room," the Chameleon offers.

Where would Hale hide his computer room? you wonder, stepping into the corridor. But, in fact, he didn't hide it. He must have been so proud of his configuration that he put it on display like Christmas decorations in a store window. Through a glass wall you can see an operator sitting at the main console.

"Got another one of those tranquilizer darts?" you ask the Chameleon.

"Just one. But that's all I need." Opening the door, he slithers into the room. As you watch, the operator joins the rest of the staff in a well-earned siesta.

"Okay, do your stuff, Orion," your teammate urges.

You nod and slip into the operator's seat. Luckily for you, ACT just gave a training session on this new supercomputer. You know exactly how to get into the superuser mode. And, with a few quick commands, you've called up Hale's data and sent it to the big bit bucket in the sky. Just to make sure, you call for a file allocation check.

"Fourteen billion bytes free storage," the status line reports.

The Chameleon's eyes widen. "Did that status line say fourteen billion bytes? How could it erase so much memory so fast?''

"It may have taken years to input all that data, but as anyone who's worked with computers knows, it takes only a few simple statements to erase it all.''

"Good work, Orion. But now we'd better get Crystal and split.''

Back in the lab, the chemist proudly shows you that the vat of bright orange solution has turned a muddy green. The odor coming from the container reminds you of a rotting swamp.

"I take it those chips are dead?'' you gag, holding your nose and backing out the door.

"Decomposing,'' she confirms with a grin. "But let's get out of here. The smell is getting to me, too. And I sure don't want to be around when our friends here wake up.''

You nod. You can't wait to get out of this creepy lab and back into the sunlight.

But when you step out into the hall, you stop, rigid with fear. Where Hale was lying unconscious just a few minutes ago, there's only clean white floor tile.

"Where'd he go?'' Crystal whispers.

The Chameleon shakes his head. "That stuff is guaranteed for at least a half hour. I don't understand how he could be up.''

Before you can speculate, a loud bell begins to sound, and then another and another.

"Oh, no!'' you cry. "He must have set off the alarm. We've got to get out of here before it's too late — if it isn't already.''

CHAPTER

14

All your instincts tell you to run. But you don't know which way to go. Without those gills, you can't leave the lab the way you came in.

"What do we do now?" you ask the Chameleon.

Before he can answer, a khaki-clad guard rounds the corner — followed by another and then another. *Great,* you think, *we've come this far, and now we're just going to get captured again.* And then you hear a steely voice only inches from your ear.

"Good work. You can turn off the alarm now," the Chameleon growls.

Your head snaps around to see him aiming the needle gun at you and Crystal. You know it's empty, but the guards fall for his bluff. They think he's one of them.

"Are you sure you can handle these two by yourself?" one of them asks.

"Certainly," the Chameleon snaps. "I've been ordered to bring them to the hotel complex for interrogation. However, this is my first shift down here. Can you tell me the fastest way back to the mainland?"

The spokesman scratches his chin. "The subs are fast, but the bubbles are faster. The launch room is at the end of the corridor."

"Thanks, buddy, I owe you one," the Chameleon says, pushing you down the hall.

Less than a minute later you're in the bubble room, which looks a lot like a subway platform. But the pit where you'd expect to see tracks is full of water. Floating in the water are several transparent plastic globes, each about the size of a helicopter cockpit. They're all tethered to the platform by nylon cord.

"Look, they must launch from over there." Crystal points toward a set of partially submerged metal doors on the other side of the water trough.

The spheres look about as substantial as soap bubbles. "Are these things really safe?" you ask, poking one. The surface of the bubble gives slightly, but feels sturdier than you expected.

"Do we really have a choice?" Crystal asks. You know exactly what she means. At any minute Al and Burt are going to wake up. And when they do, every guard in the place will know that the Chameleon is an imposter. "Besides," Crystal adds, "ACT was testing something like this when I took my deep-sea diving refresher course. They let me take the controls a few times. The only trouble is that there's usually an operator to work the door mechanism. I'll just have to set a delay and then hop inside with you."

The Chameleon pulls one of the bubbles up against the platform and opens its door. After hesitating for a moment, he steps inside.

Taking a deep breath, you follow him inside. It's a spooky feeling because there doesn't appear to be anything between you and the water.

Crystal punches in an automatic sequence and then dashes across the launch room. You wonder why she's in such a hurry until you see a transparent wall begin to rise at the edge of the dock. She barely has time to untie the bubble and scramble across the rapidly closing barrier before the room is sealed off and the water level begins to rise.

As Crystal sits down, you pull the door shut. The water slowly rises around you. If the doors at the end of the room don't open soon, your little bubble is going to pop against the ceiling, and the three of you will drown.

Suddenly, you see a look of complete horror on Crystal's face. What now? A leak in the bubble? A hitch in the automatic launch system? Or something worse?

Turning to follow the direction of Crystal's gaze, you see that, unfortunately, it's category three. Up on the platform is a crazed Damian Hale.

"What have you done to my life's work?" his voice booms into the capsule. You realize he must be talking into a hidden microphone that's relayed directly above your head. "You'll die for destroying my files."

"Don't worry," Crystal says, "he can't get to us. That automatic sequence is locked in."

As if to confirm her words, the doors on the other side of the room finally swing open and your bubble whooshes free of the lab and out into the open sea.

The menacing figure of Damian Hale disappears as the doors slide closed, but his voice is still loud and clear above your head.

"You'll never get away from me," Hale vows. "Your end is just minutes away."

CHAPTER
15

"Do you think Hale's bluffing?" Crystal asks.

The Chameleon shrugs. "I certainly hope so."

You hold your breath as the bubble slowly, slowly starts to rise. Far above, you can see sunlight.

"Can't you speed this thing up?" you ask Crystal.

"No. We've got to let ourselves adjust to the pressure change."

The sea world around you is quiet. Even Hale has signed off. All you can hear is the shallow breathing of the other passengers.

It seems as though you may have escaped Hale after all — until you see five dark shapes jetting through the water.

Uh-oh, you think. *Sharks. And they're probably not here for a water ballet.*

"Is there any defense system on this bubble?" Chameleon asks.

"Yes, there's a spear gun," Crystal answers. "But I don't know how to activate it. It's computer-controlled."

You take a deep breath and try to stay cool. "Let me at it," you say.

You and Crystal change places, and the bubble tilts wildly. Quickly, you inspect the controls. *Thank goodness, they've installed a standard keyboard,* you think.

Type in the following program which controls the spear gun. (Type each entry as one line on your computer.) The program plays a game in which sharks come at you from any direction. You have to figure out how to move your bubble and fire back in the right direction to hit them. And you must destroy all five sharks before they get you. Good luck. For some hints, see the Reference Manual, page 123.

PROGRAM 7

```
10  RANDOMIZE
20  DIM SX(5),SY(5),X2(5),Y2(5)
30  B$="O" : UL=78
40  S$=CHR$(127):CO=0
50  CLS
60  BX=40:BY=12:N=5
70  FOR I=1 TO 5
80  SX(I)=INT(UL*RND(1))+1
90  SY(I)=INT(22*RND(1))+1
100 NEXT I
```

```
110 LOCATE BY,BX: PRINT B$
120 FOR I=1 TO 5
130 LOCATE SY(I),SX(I)
140 PRINT S$
150 NEXT I
160 MI$=M$:M$=INKEY$
170 CO=CO+1
180 IF CO>5 THEN CO=1
190 IF SX(CO)=FX AND SY(CO)=FY
    THEN 450
200 X1=BX: Y1=BY
210 IF M$="A" THEN BY=BY-1:
    GOTO 320
220 IF M$="Z" THEN BY=BY+1:
    GOTO 320
230 IF M$="," THEN BX=BX-1:
    GOTO 320
240 IF M$="." THEN BX=BX+1:
    GOTO 320
250 IF FI=1 THEN GOTO 320
260 IF M$="E" THEN MO=1:GOTO 310
270 IF M$="X" THEN MO=2:GOTO 310
280 IF M$="S" THEN MO=3:GOTO 310
290 IF M$="D" THEN MO=4:GOTO 310
300 GOTO 320
310 FI=1:FX=BX:FY=BY
320 IF BX > UL THEN BX=UL:
330 IF BX < 1 THEN BX=1:
340 IF BY > 23 THEN BY=23:
350 IF BY< 1 THEN BY=1
360 LOCATE Y1,X1:PRINT " "
370 LOCATE BY,BX:PRINT B$
380 IF SX(CO)=999 THEN 560
390 X2(CO)=SX(CO): Y2(CO)=SY(CO)
```

```
400 IF SX(CO)=FX AND SY(CO)=FY
    THEN GOTO 450
410 IF BX>SX(CO) THEN SX(CO)=
    SX(CO)+1: GOTO 450
420 IF BX<SX(CO) THEN SX(CO)=
    SX(CO)-1: GOTO 450
430 IF BY>SY(CO) THEN SY(CO)=
    SY(CO)+1: GOTO 450
440 IF BY<SY(CO) THEN SY(CO)=
    SY(CO)-1
450 FOR I=1 TO 5
460 IF SX(I)=FX AND SY(I)=FY
    THEN 780
470 IF SX(I)=BX AND SY(I)=BY
    THEN 680
480 NEXT I
490 IF SX(CO)=999 THEN 560
500 IF SX(CO)>UL THEN SX(CO)=UL
510 IF SX(CO)<1 THEN SY(CO)=1
520 IF SY(CO)> 23 THEN SY(CO)=23
530 IF SY(CO)< 1 THEN SY(CO)=1
540 LOCATE Y2(CO), X2(CO):
    PRINT " "
550 LOCATE SY(CO),SX(CO):
    PRINT S$
560 IF FI<>1 THEN 160
570 X3=FX: Y3=FY
580 ON MO GOTO 590,600,610,620
590 FY=FY-1: GOTO 630
600 FY=FY+1: GOTO 630
610 FX=FX-1: GOTO 630
620 FX=FX+1
630 IF FY> 23 OR FY<1 OR FX>UL
    OR FX<1 THEN 670
```

```
640 LOCATE Y3,X3: PRINT " "
650 LOCATE FY,FX:PRINT CHR$(249)
660 GOTO 160
670 FI=0: LOCATE Y3,X3:
        PRINT " ": GOTO 160
680 FOR I=3000 TO 100 STEP -10
690 SOUND I,5.000001E-03:NEXT I
700 SOUND 32767,999
710 CLS:LOCATE 12,28:
720 PRINT "YOU WERE EATEN BY A
        SHARK!": END
730 CLS:LOCATE 10,35
740 PRINT "WOW! YOU DID IT!
        YOU DEFEATED THE SHARKS"
750 FOR I=1 TO 15
760 SOUND RND*1000+130,5
770 NEXT I:END
780 SOUND 1000,1:SX(I)=999:
        SY(I)=999
790 N=N-1: IF N=0 THEN 730
800 GOTO 470
```

IBM	Apple		Radio Shack		Commodore		TI	Atari
PC & PCjr	II+	IIe	TRS-80	Color	64	VIC-20	99/4A	400/800
✓								

This program will run as is on the IBM PC and PCjr. See the Reference Manual, page 107, for separate listings for all other computers.

86

From the way the Chameleon is gripping your shoulder, you know you're not the only one who's tense. But finally you activate the spear gun and hit all five sharks. A few moments later, you breathe a sigh of relief as the bubble surfaces.

Not far away you can see the Chameleon's boat. Marlow is at the helm, heading toward you. And lucky thing, because all that firing used up most of the bubble's power.

Marlow's about 100 yards away when suddenly another bubble pops to the surface, blocking your way. At the controls is the man you'd hoped never to see again — Damian Hale. And as you watch in horror, he starts working furiously over his keyboard.

"What's he up to?" Crystal whispers.

There's no need to answer as the hatch on your bubble begins to open. Though the hatch is above the water line, a wave hits its side, and gallons of water pour in. You know that a few more waves will sink the bubble.

"Let's swim for it," Crystal says.

"But we don't know if he's brought along more sharks," the Chameleon points out. "And he can pick us off with *his* spear gun."

"Spear gun," you say. "That's it! I think I've got one shot left. And maybe we can use it to pop Hale's bubble first."

Carefully you take aim. If you blow it now, you might as well prepare to meet Davy Jones. You push the fire button, and a spear streaks through the water toward Hale's bubble. You hear a gigantic POP. Then Hale's bubble explodes. When the spray settles, all you can see are jagged shards of plastic floating in the blue water.

"What happened to Hale?" Crystal gasps.

"We'd better not stay around to find out," the Chameleon answers with a grin. "When Big Al and Burt wake up, they're going to be madder than Hale."

As he speaks, you see that Marlow is maneuvering the sloop next to the bubble. Before you know it, you're safely on board.

The Chameleon instantly takes over as Scarf Windhammer, revealing a powerful motor on the sailboat. Within moments you're speeding away from beautiful Corona.

"Where's the senator?" Crystal asks, looking around the deck.

"Unfortunately, I had to tie him and stow him down below," Marlow answers. "I've kept him off Wungo bars since yesterday, and he's suffering withdrawal symptoms. Last night he was willing to trade the whole state of Arizona for one bite of a Wungo."

"That sounds pretty bad," Crystal says.

"Yeah. But this morning, he seems to be coming around. Now he's willing to trade Arizona only if the Armed Services Committee will put a new air force base in his home state."

Crystal nods. "You're right. That sounds more like the senator. And you'll be glad to know that when I was in Hale's lab, I figured out the connection between the bars and the chips. According to Hale's notes, the chips die if they don't receive the proper nourishment every eight hours.''

"So the senator ought to be back to normal soon," you say.

"What about the conference?" the Chameleon asks.

Marlow grins. "Funny thing. The computer that runs the whole complex wasn't feeling too well this morning and decided not to report for duty. Nothing is working around that place. So, of course, they had to move the conference to a neighboring island.''

"That means we really did it," you crow.

"Yeah," the Chameleon agrees, pounding you on the back. "Score another one for ACT.''

You turn to Marlow. "There's only one thing needed to make this mission complete.''

He quirks an eyebrow. "What's that?''

"Breakfast. It's been a long night, and Hale didn't feed us down there.''

Marlow pulls a Wungo bar out of his pocket. Before you can say "yuck," he waves his cape in front of it. And when he pulls the black cloth away, you're staring at a white-linen-covered table set for four with everything from griddle cakes to blueberry muffins.

"Breakfast for a crack ACT team is served," he announces with a flourish.

REFERENCE MANUAL

Note to user: The programming activities in this book have been designed for use with the BASIC programming language on the IBM PC and PCjr, Apple II Plus or Apple IIe (with Applesoft BASIC), Commodore 64, VIC-20, TI-99/4A, Atari 400/800, Radio Shack TRS-80 Level 2 or greater, and the Radio Shack Color Computer. Each machine has its own operating procedures for starting up BASIC and editing programs. So make sure you're in BASIC before running any of these programs, and check your user manual for instructions on how to edit lines. Also make sure you type NEW before entering each program to clear out any leftovers from previous activities.

The version of the program included in the text will generally run on most of the computers listed above. However, a few of the commands used are not available on some home systems. If the program as given does not run on one of the micros listed above, modification instructions will be included in this Reference Manual. TI-99/4A users, please note: The Texas Instruments version of regular BASIC doesn't allow multiple statements on a line or the word GOTO following a THEN. Multiple statements on the same line should be entered as one statement per line number and any THEN GOTO line number should be entered as just THEN line number.

Even if you're using a computer other than the ones mentioned, the program may still work, since it's always written in the most generalized BASIC.

If you need help with one of the computer activities in the *Micro Adventure,* or want to understand how a program works, you'll find what you need in this manual.

Naturally, programs must be typed into your computer *exactly* as given. If the program should run on your computer but you're having problems, do a list on the program and check your typing before you try anything else. Even a misplaced comma or parenthesis might cause a syntax error that will prevent the whole program from working.

TERMS YOU NEED TO KNOW

Computer experts have a special "language" they use when talking about programs. Here are some common terms that will help you understand the explanations in this manual.

Arrays are groups of two or more logically related data elements in a program that have the same name. However, so that the individual elements in the array can be used, each is also identified by its own address (called an *index* by programmers). You can think of an array as an apartment building. One hundred people might live at the Northwest Apartments (or 100 pieces of information might be stored in the NW array). But each unit within the building has a number (like Apt 14), so that it can be located and receive mail. In the NW Array, 14 could be the index to find a particular piece of information, and would be written NW(14). If you put the 26 letters of the alphabet into an array called Alpha$, then Alpha$(2) would equal "B" because B is the second letter of the alphabet.

ASCII (pronounced *asskee*) is the standard code used by most microcomputers to represent characters such as letters, numbers, and punctuation. A chart of the ASCII codes appears in the appendix to this manual.

ASC is a function in BASIC that will supply a character's ASCII code. For example, ASC("A") will give you the number 65.

Bugs are errors or mistakes in a program that keep it from doing what it's supposed to do. Some of the programming activities in this book will ask you to find and fix a bug in the program so that it will work correctly.

Functions are ready-made routines that perform standard calculations in a program. It's sort of like having a key on a calculator that computes a square root or percentage of a number. The programming language BASIC comes with a number of standard functions to perform certain tasks. For example, the function SQR(x) will find the square root of any number when x is replaced by that number. You might want to check the BASIC manual that came with your computer to see which functions are available on your system.

INT is a function that changes any number that you supply into a whole number or integer. For example, INT(4.5) will return the value 4. For numbers greater than 0, INT just throws away any fractions and supplies you with the whole number.

LEN is a function that tells you the number of characters in a string of letters, numbers, or other symbols. For example, if a variable string called A$ contained "STOP" then LEN(A$) = 4.

Loops are sections of programs that may be performed a specified number of times or until certain conditions are met. For example, if you wanted to write a program that would count from 1 to 100, a loop could be used to keep adding 1 to a counter variable until the number 100 was reached. Loops are most commonly formed with FOR/NEXT statements or GOTO commands. You'll find many examples of these in the programs in this book.

Random Number Generator This function, which is called RND in BASIC, lets you generate numbers at "random" just as though you were throwing a set of dice and didn't know which number was going to come up next. In most home computers, the RND function returns a fraction between 0 and 1. To get numbers in a larger range, the program must multiply the fraction by a larger number. For example, RND * 10 will produce numbers between 0 and 10.

REM. This command is used to tell the computer that whatever is on a particular line is just a comment and should not be executed. An example might look like this:

```
10  REM  THIS PROGRAM COUNTS DOWN
```

Strings are groups of one or more letters, numbers, or other symbols that are treated as a unit. In the English language, a collection of letters that make up a word can be thought of as a string. In a program, the information in a string is often enclosed in quotation marks to let the computer know that the symbols are to be treated as characters. In the string "123" the program is dealing with the characters 1, 2, and 3, not the larger number 123. The computer is storing these as the ASCII values for 1, 2, and 3, which are 49, 50, and 51. A string that is empty and has no characters in it is called a null string and is represented as " ".

Variables are names used to represent values that will change during the course of a program. For example, a variable named D$ might represent any day of the week. It may help you to think of a variable as a storage box, waiting to receive whatever information you want to put in. Variables that deal with strings of symbols are always followed by a dollar sign. Variables that end in a percent sign always hold integers (the whole numbers like 1, 2, 3, 500). Variables with a pound sign or no special character at the end hold numbers that may contain fractions. The number of characters allowed in a variable name varies from computer to computer.

PROGRAM 1: DECODE MESSAGE

Modifications for Other Micros

Atari — Make these changes:
```
5 DIM B$(30),A$(30),M$(30),
    N$(30),R$(1)
90 IF M$(I,I+1)=A$(K,K+1)
    THEN 110
110 N$(LEN(N$)+1)=B$(K,K+1)
```

TI-99/4A — Make these changes:
```
90 IF SEG$(M$,I,1)=SEG$(A$,K,1)
    THEN 110
110 N$=N$ & SEG$(B$,K,1)
```

What the Program Does

In order to receive your mission instructions from ACT, you must decode their scrambled message. When you run the program and type in the garbled message using all capital letters, the program will automatically decode it.

How the Program Works

The message is scrambled because a key substitution code has been used. Here's how it works. Notice that the letters of the alphabet appear in order in line 10 of the program. In line 20 there is a key word — in this case SUN, followed by the remaining letters of the alphabet in order (omitting the letters S, U, and N). To decode the message by hand, you would write out the two alphabets in the same way. Looking at the two lines, you can see that the code letter for A is S. The code letter for B is U. The code letter for C is N. And the code letter for D is A. The rest of the alphabet follows, omitting the letters in the key word.

Using these substitutions, the program can decode the encoded message automatically.

The message must be stored by the program so it can be decoded. In this case, it's being stored in a variable named M$.

In order to get a readable message, the program must look at each character in the message in turn and substitute the corresponding decoded letter.

Can you tell which lines in the program do this? It's lines 70 through 120.

Decoded, the message reads:

URGENT
ORION DO NOTHING TO STOP
THIS HIJACKING

PROGRAM 2: WORD ASSOCIATION

Modifications for Other Micros

Atari — Make these changes:

```
5 DIM Q$(15),A$(15),W$(15)
150 PRINT CHR$(123)
200 PRINT CHR$(0)
```

Commodore 64 and VIC-20 — Make these changes:

```
150 PRINT CHR$(97)
200 PRINT CHR$(115)
```

TI-99/4A, Radio Shack, and Apple — Make these changes:

```
150 PRINT CHR$(45)
200 PRINT CHR$(43)
```

What the Program Does

When the program is run, 10 words are displayed one at a time on the screen. To score 10 points and save your life, you must supply the correct antonym for each. Since BRUTE isn't always looking for the obvious antonym, you probably won't get all of them right unless you look at the data statements in the program.

How the Program Works

The program uses a variable called Q$ to hold the quiz words and another called A$ to hold the corresponding answers. To figure out what correct answer goes with each quiz word, you must understand how the data is read into the variables. See line 80. Yes, each quiz word in the data statement is followed by the answer BRUTE is looking for. When you play the game, you get one point for each correct antonym and also some graphics feedback on the video game. Answers must be typed in capital letters.

PROGRAM 3: SHARK TANK CONTROL

Modifications for Other Micros

TI-99/4A — Make these changes:
```
20 CALL CLEAR
82 FOR N=1 TO 10 STEP 5
84 CALL HCHAR(I,N,126,4)
86 CALL HCHAR(I,N+4,62,1)
90 NEXT N
100 SOUND(500,131,10,123,10)
110 FOR J=1 TO 100
180 CALL HCHAR(I,1,35,10)
200 CALL HCHAR(I-K,1,35,10)
Remove line 220
```

Apple — Make these changes:
```
20 HOME
100 PRINT CHR$(7), CHR$(7)
180 VTAB I: HTAB 1:
      PRINT "################"
200 VTAB I-K: HTAB 1:
      PRINT "################"
220 VTAB 1: HTAB 25
```

Commodore 64 — Make these changes:
```
10 POKE 54296,15:POKE 54277,90:
      POKE 54278,200,POKE 54276,17
20 PRINT CHR$(147)
90 PRINT ">--->---->"
100 POKE 54273,2: POKE 54272,37
105 POKE 54273,2: POKE 54272,6
135 POKE 54296,0
180 PRINT CHR$(145);"##########"
200 PRINT CHR$(145);"##########"
REMOVE LINE 220
```

99

VIC-20 — Same as Commodore 64 except remove line 100 and 105 or substitute VIC-20 sound addresses in poke commands:

```
10 POKE 36878,15
100 POKE 36874,195
105 POKE 36874,191
135 POKE 36874,0
```

Radio Shack Color Computer — Make these changes:

```
40 PRINT "##########"
REMOVE  LINE 70
90 PRINT @ (I-1)*32,"****>****>"
100 SOUND 89,5: SOUND 78,5
180 PRINT @ I*32,"##########"
200 PRINT @(I-K)*32,"##########"
REMOVE LINE 220
230 PRINT @5,"YOU'VE MADE IT TO
       SAFETY"
```

Radio Shack TRS-80 — Same as Color Computer but also remove line 100.

```
40 PRINT "##########"
REMOVE  LINE 70
90 PRINT @ (I-1)*64,"****>****>"
REMOVE LINE 100
180 PRINT @ I*64,"##########"
200 PRINT @(I-K)*64,"##########"
REMOVE LINE 220
230 PRINT @5,"YOU'VE MADE IT TO
       SAFETY"
```

100

Atari — Make these changes:

```
20 GRAPHICS 0
90 PRINT "---->---->---->"
100 SOUND 0,121,10,4:
      SOUND 0,128,10,4
105 SOUND 0,0,0,0,
180 POSITION 1,I:
      PRINT "################"
200 POSITION 1,I-K:
      PRINT "################"
220 POSITION 25,1
```

What the Program Does

This program controls the mechanism that rolls back the arcade floor. You must stop the floor before you drop into the shark tank.

How the Program Works

Lines 80 through 130 are a loop that opens the floor. In the program, line 80 tells the floor how far to open. To stop it, you must change the limit to a lower number.

To stop the floor at the very last minute, line 80 must read: **80 FOR I=1 TO 8**
(Actually 8 can be any number greater than 1 and less than 11. Different numbers will stop the floor at different lines on the screen.)

Later, your task is to close the floor and unlock the exit so that you can escape. You use the same program.

Lines 190 through 210 are used to accomplish this. To close the floor and unlock the door, you must modify line 190 by setting the limit of the loop to the same number that you used in line 80. (In our example it's 8.)

PROGRAM 4: SONAR

Modifications for Other Micros

Apple — Make these changes:
```
10 REM
30 X=INT(RND(1)*5)+1
40 Y=INT(RND(1)*5)+1
```

Atari — Make these changes:
```
10 REM
30 X=INT(RND(0)*5)+1
40 Y=INT(RND(0)*5)+1
```

Commodore 64 and VIC-20 — Make these changes:
```
10 REM
30 X=INT(RND(1)*5)+1
40 Y=INT(RND(1)*5)+1
```

Radio Shack — Make these changes:
```
10 REM
30 X=RND(5)
40 Y=RND(5)
```

TI-99/4A — Make these changes:
```
230 IF H < H1 THEN 240
232 PRINT "MASS IS LESS DENSE"
234 GOTO 250
240 PRINT "MASS IS DENSER"
```

102

What the Program Does

To the naked eye, you appear to be facing an underwater cliff of solid rock. You know the entrance to the lab is hidden somewhere in that cliff. But there's no way to tell where. This program plays a game in which you can locate the entrance by taking "sonar readings," and using that information to determine your next move on a five by five grid that represents the cliff. The entrance is located in the least dense section of the rock. Reading of "mass is less dense" means you're getting closer.

How the Program Works

The program uses a random number generator to select a square on the grid where the entrance is located. Also, a random number between 1 and 10 determines how many guesses you get. You start in the center of the cliff at location 3,3 on the grid. To move up, you press the number 1 on the keyboard. To move down, you press 2. To move right, you press 3. And to move left, you press 4. Using the absolute value function, ABS, the program calculates whether you are closer to the entrance than you were at your last position. If you're closer, it will print "mass is less dense." If you're farther away, it will print "mass is denser."

PROGRAM 5: GUEST RECORDS

Modifications for Other Micros

Atari — Make this change:
```
5 DIM C$(15),R$(3),N$(15)
```

TI-99/4A — Make these changes:
```
130 RESTORE
132 FOR J=1 TO 10
134 READ T$
136 NEXT J
200 IF CHR$(N1+48)<>SEG$(R$,1,1)
    THEN 180
205 X=1
210 GOTO 180
220 IF X <> 1 THEN 150
225 PRINT N$
260 IF A$ <> "Y" THEN 290
290 END
```

Apple, Commodore 64 and VIC-20, Radio Shack TRS-80 and Color Computer — Since the Apple, Commodore, and Radio Shack computers do not have the selective restore option, it is necessary to read past the first 10 data items when processing additional requests. Lines 130–136 below should be added to thè program for these computers.
```
130 RESTORE
132 FOR J=1 TO 10
134 READ T$
136 NEXT J
```

What the Program Does

Because guests pay for everything at the Corona resort by computer, it's easy to find out exactly which services they've used. This program does an audit of 10 different services to see who has used them.

Marlow has supplied the names of four guests he is sure are under control. You can use this program to find out which single service all of them have used.

How the Program Works

The services you will be examining are listed in lines 20 and 30. Each service is represented by a specific number code in lines 90 through 110. Room service is represented by 1. The movie is represented by 2, etc. When you run the program, you select services to audit one at a time. The program sorts through the charge slips for the guests in question, which are represented in lines 40 through 70. It then prints out the names of the guests who have used that service. You can audit the services in any order — until you find the one that all four of these guests have used. That's the best place to start looking for the mind control activity.

PROGRAM 6: LAB DOOR SECURITY

Modifications for Other Micros

Atari — Atari BASIC does not allow string arrays, so you'll need to treat the four devils from the sea as one big string.

```
10 REM
20 DIM K(2), D$(50)
Remove line 30
60 D$="OCTOPUS*****PIRANHA*****
      BARRACUDA***ELECTRIC EEL"
110 N=INT(RND(1)*4)
112 N=N*12+1
114 PRINT "RELEASE",D$(N,12)
140 PRINT "SO FAR, SO GOOD"
```

Apple — Make this change:
```
REMOVE 10
```

Radio Shack TRS-80 and Color Computer — Make these changes:
```
10 REM
110 PRINT "RELEASE",D$(RND(4))
```

Commodore 64 and VIC-20 — Make this change:
```
10 REM
```

What the Program Does

This program protects the entrance to Hale's underwater laboratory with a two-symbol key lock. The penalty for not knowing the right code is death — by a variety of ghastly alternatives.

How the Program Works

The program asks you to press two of three symbols — @, #, or $. You must also get them in the correct order. From lines 40, 50, and 100, you can tell that it's looking for the characters whose ASCII values are 36 and 35. Check the ASCII chart on page 125 to see which symbols these represent. Or, since you're able to list the program, you can change lines 40 and 50 to look for any symbols you wish. Either way, you avoid Hale's death trap.

PROGRAM 7: SHARK ATTACK

Complete Listings for All Other Micros

Apple Version

```
10 DIM SX(5),SY(5),X2(5),Y2(5)
20 B$="O":UL=39:LL=23
40 S$=CHR$(62):CO=0
50 HOME
60 BX=40:BY=12:N=5
70 FOR I=1 TO 5
80 SX(I)=INT(38*RND(1))+1
82 SY(I)=INT(22*RND(1))+1
90 NEXT I
100 HTAB BX: VTAB BY: PRINT B$
110 FOR I=1 TO 5
112 HTAB SX(I): VTAB SY(I)
114 PRINT S$
116 NEXT I
120 MI$=M$:M=PEEK(-16384)
```

```
122 IF M >128 THEN POKE -16368,0:
    M$=CHR$(M-128):GOTO 130
125 M$=" "
130 CO=CO+1
140 IF CO>5 THEN CO=1
150 X1=BX: Y1=BY
160 IF M$="A" THEN BY=BY-1:
    GOTO 260
170 IF M$="Z" THEN BY=BY+1:
    GOTO 260
180 IF M$="," THEN BX=BX-1:
    GOTO 260
190 IF M$="." THEN BX=BX+1:
    GOTO 260
200 IF FI=1 THEN GOTO 260
210 IF M$="E" THEN MO=1:GOTO 250
220 IF M$="X" THEN MO=2:GOTO 250
230 IF M$="S" THEN MO=3:GOTO 250
240 IF M$="D" THEN MO=4:GOTO 250
245 GOTO 260
250 FI=1:FX=BX:FY=BY
260 IF BX > 39 THEN BX=39:
270 IF BX < 1 THEN BX=1:
280 IF BY > 23 THEN BY=23:
290 IF BY< 1 THEN BY=1
300 HTAB X1: VTAB Y1: PRINT " "
310 HTAB BX: VTAB BY: PRINT B$
320 IF SX(CO)=999 THEN 490
330 X2(CO)=SX(CO): Y2(CO)=SY(CO)
335 IF SX(CO)=FX AND SY(C0)=FY
    THEN 380
340 IF BX>SX(CO) THEN SX(CO)=
    SX(CO)+1: GOTO 380
```

```
350  IF BX<SX(CO) THEN SX(CO)=
     SX(CO)-1: GOTO 380
360  IF BY>SY(CO) THEN SY(CO)=
     SY(CO)+1: GOTO 380
370  IF BY<SY(CO) THEN SY(CO)=
     SY(CO)-1
380  FOR I=1 TO 5
390  IF SX(I)=FX AND SY(I)=FY
     THEN 630
400  IF SX(I)=BX AND SY(I)=BY
     THEN 600
410  NEXT I
420  IF SX(CO)=999 THEN 490
430  IF SX(CO)>39 THEN SX(CO)=39
440  IF SX(CO)<1 THEN SY(CO)=1
450  IF SY(CO)> 23 THEN SY(CO)=23
460  IF SY(CO)< 1 THEN SY(CO)=1
470  HTAB X2(CO): VTAB Y2(CO):
     PRINT " "
480  HTAB SX(CO): VTAB SY(CO):
     PRINT S$
490  IF FI<>1 THEN 120
500  X3=FX: Y3=FY
510  ON MO GOTO 515,520,530,540
515  FY=FY-1: GOTO 550
520  FY=FY+1: GOTO 550
530  FX=FX-1: GOTO 550
540  FX=FX+1
550  IF FY> 23 OR FY<1 THEN 590
555  IF FX>39 OR FX<1 THEN 590
560  HTAB X3: VTAB Y3: PRINT " "
570  HTAB FX: VTAB FY : PRINT "*"
580  GOTO 120
```

```
590 FI=0: HTAB X3: VTAB Y3:
    PRINT " "
595 GOTO 120
600 FOR I=1 TO 10: PRINT CHR$(7):
    NEXT I
610 HOME: HTAB 9: VTAB 12: FLASH:
612 PRINT "YOU WERE EATEN BY A
    SHARK!":NORMAL
614 FOR I=1 TO 500: NEXT I: END
620 HOME:FLASH:SPEED=1:HTAB 15:
    VTAB 10:
622 PRINT "WOW! YOU DEFEATED
    THE SHARKS"
624 NORMAL: SPEED=255
626 FOR I=1 TO 10: PRINT CHR$(7)
627 NEXT I:END
630 PRINT CHR$(7): HTAB SX(I):
    VTAB SY(I)
632 PRINT " "
634 SX(I)=999:SY(I)=999
640 N=N-1: IF N=0 THEN 620
650 GOTO 400
```

Atari Version
```
5 OPEN #1,4,0,"K:"
10 GRAPHICS 0: POKE 752,1:
   SETCOLOR 2,0,0:SETCOLOR 4,0,0
20 DIM SX(5),SY(5),X2(5),Y2(5),
   B$(1),S$(1),M$(1),MI$(1)
30 B$="O" : UL=39: LL=21
40 S$=CHR$(62):CO=0
50 BX=20:BY=12:N=5
60 FOR I=1 TO 5
```

```
70  SX(I)=INT(UL*RND(1))+1
80  SY(I)=INT(LL*RND(1))+1
90  NEXT I
100 POSITION BX,BY: PRINT B$
110 FOR I=1 TO 5
120 POSITION BX,BY
130 PRINT S$
140 NEXT I
150 IF PEEK(764)<>255 THEN 160
155 MI$=M$
157 GET #1,M:M$=CHR$(M)
160 IF FI=1 THEN POKE 764,255
170 CO=CO+1
180 IF CO>5 THEN CO=1
190 X1=BX: Y1=BY
200 IF M$="A" THEN BY=BY-1:
        GOTO 310
210 IF M$="Z" THEN BY=BY+1:
        GOTO 310
220 IF M$="," THEN BX=BX-1:
        GOTO 310
230 IF M$="." THEN BX=BX+1:
        GOTO 310
240 IF FI=1 THEN GOTO 310
250 IF M$="E" THEN MO=1:GOTO 300
260 IF M$="X" THEN MO=2:GOTO 300
270 IF M$="S" THEN MO=3:GOTO 300
280 IF M$="D" THEN MO=4:GOTO 300
290 GOTO 310
300 FI=1:FX=BX:FY=BY
310 IF BX > UL THEN BX=UL
320 IF BX < 1 THEN BX=1
330 IF BY > LL THEN BY=LL
```

```
340 IF BY< 1 THEN BY=1
350 POSITION X1,Y1 :PRINT " "
360 POSITION BX,BY:PRINT B$
370 IF SX(CO)=999 THEN 550
380 X2(CO)=SX(CO): Y2(CO)=SY(CO)
390 IF SX(CO)=FX AND SY(CO)=FY
    THEN GOTO 440
400 IF BX>SX(CO) THEN SX(CO)=
    SX(CO)+1: GOTO 440
410 IF BX<SX(CO) THEN SX(CO)=
    SX(CO)-1: GOTO 440
420 IF BY>SY(CO) THEN SY(CO)=
    SY(CO)+1: GOTO 440
430 IF BY<SY(CO) THEN SY(CO)=SY(CO)
440 FOR I=1 TO 5
450 IF SX(I)=FX AND SY(I)=FY THEN 77
460 IF SX(I)=BX AND SY(I)=BY THEN 67
470 NEXT I
480 IF SX(CO)=999 THEN 550
490 IF SX(CO)>UL THEN SX(CO)=UL
500 IF SX(CO)<1. THEN SY(CO)=1
510 IF SY(CO)> LL THEN SY(CO)=LL
520 IF SY(CO)< 1 THEN SY(CO)=1
530 POSITION X2(CO),Y2(CO):
    PRINT " "
540 POSITION SX(CO),SY(CO):
    PRINT S$
550 IF FI<>1 THEN 150
560 X3=FX: Y3=FY
570 ON MO GOTO 580,590,600,610
580 FY=FY-1: GOTO 620
590 FY=FY+1: GOTO 620
600 FX=FX-1: GOTO 620
610 FX=FX+1
```

112

```
620 IF FY> LL OR FY<1 OR
       FX>UL OR FX<1 THEN 660
630 POSITION X3,Y3: PRINT " "
640 POSITION FX,FY: PRINT "+"
650 GOTO 150
660 FI=0: POSITION X3,Y3:
       PRINT " ": GOTO 150
670 SOUND 0,121,10,4:
       SOUND 0,128,10,4
680 SOUND 0,0,0,0
690 GRAPHICS 0: POSITION 7,12
700 PRINT "YOU WERE EATEN BY A
       SHARK!": END
710 GRAPHICS 0: POSITION 4,12
720 PRINT "WOW! YOU DID IT!
       YOU DEFEATED THE SHARKS"
730 FOR N=255 TO 20 STEP -5:
       FOR V=8 TO 0 STEP -3
740 SOUND 0,N-1,10,V: SOUND
       1,N,10,V
750 SOUND 2,N+1,10,V
760 NEXT V: NEXT N:
770 FOR J=1 TO 255 STEP 50
780 SOUND 0,J,10,10: NEXT J
790 SOUND 0,0,0,0:SX(I)=999
800 N=N-1: IF N=0 THEN 710
810 GOTO 460
```

Commodore 64 Version

```
 10 DIM SX(5),SY(5),X2(5),Y2(5)
 20 Z$="                        "  '
 CLR/HOME + 22 CURSOR DOWN ARROWS
 30 B$="O":UL=37:LL=22
 40 S$=CHR$(127):CO=0
```

```
50 PRINT CHR$(147)
60 BX=20:BY=12:N=5
70 FOR I=1 TO 5
80 SX(I)=INT(UL*RND(1))
90 SY(I)=INT(LL*RND(1))
100 NEXT I
110 PRINT LEFT$(Z$,BY);TAB(BX);B$
120 FOR I=1 TO 5
130 PRINT LEFT$(Z$,SY(I));
     TAB((SX(I))
140 PRINT S$
150 NEXT I
160 MI$=M$:GET M$
170 CO=CO+1
180 IF CO>5 THEN CO=1
190 X1=BX: Y1=BY
200 IF M$="A" THEN BY=BY-1:
     GOTO 310
210 IF M$="Z" THEN BY=BY+1:
     GOTO 310
220 IF M$="," THEN BX=BX-1:
     GOTO 310
230 IF M$="." THEN BX=BX+1:
     GOTO 310
240 IF FI=1 THEN GOTO 310
250 IF M$="E" THEN MO=1:GOTO 300
260 IF M$="X" THEN MO=2:GOTO 300
270 IF M$="S" THEN MO=3:GOTO 300
280 IF M$="D" THEN MO=4:GOTO 300
290 GOTO 310
300 FI=1:FX=BX:FY=BY
310 IF BX > UL THEN BX=UL:
320 IF BX < 1 THEN BX=1:
330 IF BY > LL THEN BY=LL:
```

114

```
340 IF BY< 1 THEN BY=1
350 PRINT LEFT$(Z$,Y1);
    TAB(X1);" "
360 PRINT LEFT$(Z$,BY);
    TAB(BX); B$
370 IF SX(CO)=999 THEN 550
380 X2(CO)=SX(CO): Y2(CO)=SY(CO)
390 IF SX(CO)=FX AND SY(CO)=FY
    THEN GOTO 440
400 IF BX>SX(CO) THEN SX(CO)=
    SX(CO)+1: GOTO 440
410 IF BX<SX(CO) THEN SX(CO)=
    SX(CO)-1: GOTO 440
420 IF BY>SY(CO) THEN SY(CO)=
    SY(CO)+1: GOTO 440
430 IF BY<SY(CO) THEN SY(CO)=
    SY(CO)-1
440 FOR I=1 TO 5
450 IF SX(I)=FX AND SY(I)=
    FY THEN 700
460 IF SX(I)=BX AND SY(I)=
    BY THEN 670
470 NEXT I
480 IF SX(CO)=999 AND THEN 550
490 IF SX(CO)>UL THEN SX(CO)=UL
500 IF SX(CO)<1 THEN SY(CO)=1
510 IF SY(CO)> LL THEN SY(CO)=LL
520 IF SY(CO)< 1 THEN SY(CO)=1
530 PRINT LEFT$(Z$,Y2(CO));
    TAB(X2(CO)); " "
540 PRINT LEFT$(Z$,SY(CO));
    TAB(SX(CO)); S$
550 IF FI<>1 THEN 160
560 X3=FX: Y3=FY
```

115

```
570 ON MO GOTO 580,590,600,610
580 FY=FY-1: GOTO 620
590 FY=FY+1: GOTO 620
600 FX=FX-1: GOTO 620
610 FX=FX+1
620 IF FY> LL OR FY<1 OR FX>UL
    OR FX<1 THEN 660
630 PRINT LEFT$(Z$,Y3);
    TAB(X3); " "
640 PRINT LEFT$(Z$,FY);
    TAB(FX); "+"
650 GOTO 160
660 FI=0: PRINT LEFT$(Z$,Y3);
    TAB(X3); " ": GOTO 160
670 PRINT CHR$(19); "YOU WERE
    EATEN BY A SHARK!": END
680 PRINT "WOW! YOU DID IT!
    YOU DEFEATED THE SHARKS"
690 END
700 SX(I)=999:SY(I)=999
710 POKE 54296,15: POKE 54277,90:
    POKE 54278,200
720 POKE 54273,34: POKE 54272,75
730 POKE 54276,33:
740 FOR ZZ=1 TO 200: NEXT ZZ
750 POKE 54296,0
760 N=N-1: IF N=0 THEN 680
770 GOTO 460
```

Vic-20 — The program is the same as Commodore 64 except for the following changes:

```
15 POKE 36878,15
30 B$="O":UL=21:LL=22
710 POKE 36874,195:
```

```
715 FOR LZ=1 TO 50: NEXT LZ
718 POKE 36874,0
```

Radio Shack Color Computer Version

```
10 DIM SX(5),SY(5),X2(5),Y2(5)
20 B$="O" : UL=31:LL=15
30 S$=CHR$(129):CO=0
40 CLS
50 BX=20:BY=12:N=5
60 FOR I=1 TO 5
70 SX(I)=RND(UL)
80 SY(I)=RND(LL)
90 NEXT I
100 PRINT @ BY*32+BX, B$
110 FOR I=1 TO 5
120 PRINT @ SY(I)*32+SX(I),S$
130 NEXT I
140 MI$=M$:M$=INKEY$
150 CO=CO+1
160 IF CO>5 THEN CO=1
170 IF SX(CO)=FX AND SY(CO)=
    FY THEN 430
180 X1=BX: Y1=BY
190 IF M$="A" THEN BY=BY-1:
    GOTO 300
200 IF M$="Z" THEN BY=BY+1:
    GOTO 300
210 IF M$="," THEN BX=BX-1:
    GOTO 300
220 IF M$="." THEN BX=BX+1:
    GOTO 300
230 IF FI=1 THEN GOTO 300
240 IF M$="E" THEN MO=1:GOTO 290
```

117

```
250 IF M$="X" THEN MO=2:GOTO 290
260 IF M$="S" THEN MO=3:GOTO 290
270 IF M$="D" THEN MO=4:GOTO 290
280 GOTO 300
290 FI=1:FX=BX:FY=BY
300 IF BX > UL THEN BX=UL:
310 IF BX < 0 THEN BX=0:
320 IF BY > LL THEN BY=LL:
330 IF BY< 0 THEN BY=0
340 PRINT @ 32*Y1+X1, " "
350 PRINT @ 32*BY+BX, B$
360 IF SX(CO)=999 THEN 540
370 X2(CO)=SX(CO): Y2(CO)=SY(CO)
380 IF SX(CO)=FX AND SY(CO)=FY
    THEN GOTO 430
390 IF BX>SX(CO) THEN SX(CO)=
    SX(CO)+1: GOTO 430
400 IF BX<SX(CO) THEN SX(CO)=
    SX(CO)-1: GOTO 430
410 IF BY>SY(CO) THEN SY(CO)=
    SY(CO)+1: GOTO 430
420 IF BY<SY(CO) THEN SY(CO)=
    SY(CO)-1
430 FOR I=1 TO 5
440 IF SX(I)=FX AND SY(I)=FY
    THEN 760
450 IF SX(I)=BX AND SY(I)=BY
    THEN 660
460 NEXT I
470 IF SX(CO)=999 THEN 540
480 IF SX(CO)>UL THEN SX(CO)=UL
490 IF SX(CO)<1 THEN SY(CO)=1
500 IF SY(CO)> LL THEN SY(CO)=LL
510 IF SY(CO)< 1 THEN SY(CO)=1
520 PRINT @ 32*Y2(CO)+ X2(CO), " "
```

```
530 PRINT @32*SY(CO)+SX(CO), S$
540 IF FI<>1 THEN 140
550 X3=FX: Y3=FY
560 ON MO GOTO 570,580,590,600
570 FY=FY-1: GOTO 610
580 FY=FY+1: GOTO 610
590 FX=FX-1: GOTO 610
600 FX=FX+1
610 IF FY> LL OR FY<1 OR FX>UL
      OR FX<1 THEN 650
620 PRINT @ 32*Y3+X3, " "
630 PRINT @ 32*FY+FX, "+"
640 GOTO 140
650 FI=0: PRINT @32*Y3+X3, " ":
      GOTO 140
660 FOR I=244 TO 125 STEP -5
670 SOUND I,1:NEXT I
680 SOUND 32767,999
690 CLS(0):
700 PRINT @ 74,"YOU WERE EATEN BY
      A SHARK!": END
710 CLS
720 PRINT "WOW! YOU DID IT!   YOU
      DEFEATED THE SHARKS"
730 FOR I=1 TO 15
740 SOUND RND(155)+75,5
750 NEXT I:END
760 SOUND 32,1:SX(I)=999:
770 N=N-1: IF N=0 THEN 710
780 GOTO 450
```

Radio Shack TRS-80 Version

```
10 DIM SX(5),SY(5),X2(5),Y2(5)
20 B$="O" : UL=63:LL=15
```

```
30 S$=CHR$(129):CO=0
40 CLS
50 BX=40:BY=12:N=5
60 FOR I=1 TO 5
70 SX(I)=RND(UL)
80 SY(I)=RND(LL)
90 NEXT I
100 PRINT @BY*64+BX, B$
110 FOR I=1 TO 5
120 PRINT @SY(I)*64+SX(I),S$
130 NEXT I
140 MI$=M$:M$=INKEY$
150 CO=CO+1
160 IF CO>5 THEN CO=1
170 IF SX(CO)=FX AND SY(CO)=FY
      THEN 430
180 X1=BX: Y1=BY
190 IF M$="A" THEN BY=BY-1:
      GOTO 300
200 IF M$="Z" THEN BY=BY+1:
      GOTO 300
210 IF M$="," THEN BX=BX-1:
      GOTO 300
220 IF M$="." THEN BX=BX+1:
      GOTO 300
230 IF FI=1 THEN GOTO 300
240 IF M$="E" THEN MO=1:GOTO 290
250 IF M$="X" THEN MO=2:GOTO 290
260 IF M$="S" THEN MO=3:GOTO 290
270 IF M$="D" THEN MO=4:GOTO 290
280 GOTO 300
290 FI=1:FX=BX:FY=BY
300 IF BX > UL THEN BX=UL:
310 IF BX < 0 THEN BX=0:
```

```
320 IF BY > LL THEN BY=LL:
330 IF BY< 0 THEN BY=0
340 PRINT @64*Y1+X1, " "
350 PRINT @64*BY+BX, B$
360 IF SX(CO)=999 AND THEN 540
370 X2(CO)=SX(CO): Y2(CO)=SY(CO)
380 IF SX(CO)=FX AND SY(CO)=FY
    THEN GOTO 430
390 IF BX>SX(CO) THEN SX(CO)=
    SX(CO)+1: GOTO 430
400 IF BX<SX(CO) THEN SX(CO)=
    SX(CO)-1: GOTO 430
410 IF BY>SY(CO) THEN SY(CO)=
    SY(CO)+1: GOTO 430
420 IF BY<SY(CO) THEN SY(CO)=
    SY(CO)-1
430 FOR I=1 TO 5
440 IF SX(I)=FX AND SY(I)=
    FY THEN 760
450 IF SX(I)=BX AND SY(I)=
    BY THEN 660
460 NEXT I
470 IF SX(CO)=999 THEN 540
480 IF SX(CO)>UL THEN SX(CO)=UL
490 IF SX(CO)<0 THEN SY(CO)=0
500 IF SY(CO)> LL THEN SY(CO)=LL
510 IF SY(CO)< 0 THEN SY(CO)=0
520 PRINT @64*Y2(CO)+ X2(CO), " "
530 PRINT @64*SY(CO)+SX(CO), S$
540 IF FI<>1 THEN 140
550 X3=FX: Y3=FY
560 ON MO GOTO 570,580,590,600
570 FY=FY-1: GOTO 610
580 FY=FY+1: GOTO 610
```

```
590 FX=FX-1: GOTO 610
600 FX=FX+1
610 IF FY> LL OR FY<1 OR FX>UL
    OR FX<1 THEN 650
620 PRINT @64*Y3+X3, " "
630 PRINT @64*FY+FX, "+"
640 GOTO 140
650 FI=0: PRINT @64*Y3+X3, " ":
    GOTO 140
690 CLS:
700 PRINT @74,"YOU WERE EATEN BY
    A SHARK!": END
710 CLS
720 PRINT "WOW! YOU DID IT!
    YOU DEFEATED THE SHARKS"
750 END
760 SX(I)=999:SY(I)=999
770 N=N-1: IF N=0 THEN 710
780 GOTO 450
```

TI-99/4A Version

```
10 P=10
20 A=INT(RND*4)+1
30 CALL CLEAR
40 ON A GOSUB 180,210,240,290
50 PRINT "COMMAND"
60 INPUT C
70 IF A<>C THEN GOTO 160
80 ON C GOSUB 210,180,290,240
90 PRINT "YOU KILLED A SHARK!!!"
100 FOR I=1 TO 300
110 NEXT I
120 P=P-1
130 IF P > 0 THEN GOTO 20
```

```
140 PRINT "WOW! YOU DEFEATED
    THE SHARKS!"
150 END
160 PRINT "OH NO! YOU WERE EATEN
    BY A SHARK."
170 END
180 FOR I=1 TO 10: PRINT: NEXT I
190 PRINT "**********>"
200 RETURN
210 FOR I=1 TO 10: PRINT: NEXT I
220 PRINT TAB(10) "<**********"
230 RETURN
240 FOR I=1 TO 10: PRINT
    TAB(10) "*"
250 NEXT I
260 PRINT TAB(9) "***"
270 PRINT TAB(10) "*"
280 RETURN
290 FOR I=1 TO 10: PRINT: NEXT I
300 PRINT TAB(10) "*"
310 PRINT TAB(9) "***"
320 FOR I=1 TO 10: PRINT
    TAB(10) "*"
330 NEXT I
340 RETURN
```

Note: For IBM PCjr with 40-column screen:

**set UL=38 in line 30 of IBM
    version**

What the Program Does

Using this program, you get to play a real
live "arcade-type" game. There are five sharks
coming at you from all directions. If they burst

your bubble, it's curtains for you and the rest of the ACT team. You can steer your bubble up, down, right, and left if you can figure out which input keys the program is looking for. But to get out alive, you also have to find out how to use the spear gun to wipe out those killer sharks. The spear gun can fire in all four directions if you press the right keys.

TI-99/4A version works differently. Ten sharks come at you from any direction, and you must fire back and kill them to survive.

How the Program Works

Your bubble is represented as an O on the screen and its location is controlled by the values of the variables BX that give the column and BY that give the row. The locations of the five sharks are contained in the arrays SX and SY. M$ is the key you press to make the bubble move or fire a shot from your spear gun. To find out what keys move the bubble, look at lines 210–240. An "A" will move the bubble up one row; "Z" will move it down one row; a "," will move it over one to the left; and a "." will move it over one to the right. The firing controls (defined in lines 260–290) are: E — shoot up, X — shoot down, S — shoot left, and D — shoot right.

TI-99/4A Version
Use these firing commands: 1 — fire left, 2 — fire right, 3 — fire up, 4 — fire down.

APPENDIX

ASCII Code	Character
0-32	Special system control characters
32	Space (will look blank)
33	!
34	"
35	#
36	$
37	%
38	&
39	'
40	(
41	)
42	*
43	+
44	,
45	–
46	.
47	/
48	0
49	1
50	2
51	3
52	4
53	5
54	6
55	7
56	8
57	9
58	:
59	;

60	<	79	O
61	=	80	P
62	>	81	Q
63	?	82	R
64	@	83	S
65	A	84	T
66	B	85	U
67	C	86	V
68	D	87	W
69	E	88	X
70	F	89	Y
71	G	90	Z
72	H	91	[
73	I	92	\
74	J	93	]
75	K	94	^
76	L	95	—
77	M	96	
78	N		

97-122   lower case letters

126-255   alternate character set — on some computers these codes are used to represent graphic symbols. Check the ASCII chart in the back of your computer's user guide for what these codes mean on your system.